Jane

Julie Charette

My History Log

Knowledge and Activities B

History and Citizenship Education
Secondary Cycle One

鎮欣荣

Translation by Louisa Blair,
Bob Chodos and Jean-Pierre Fournier

shkatz@
lbpearson.ca

LES ÉDITIONS
CEC

9001, boul. Louis-H.-La Fontaine, Anjou (Québec) Canada H1J 2C5
Telephone: 514-351-6010 • Fax: 514 351-3534

ENGLISH VERSION

Editorial Manager
Maryse Bérubé

Production Manager
Danielle Latendresse

Coordination Manager
Rodolphe Courcy

Project Editor
Louisa Blair for Interscript

Translators
Louisa Blair, Bob Chodos, Jean-Pierre Fournier

Proofreaders
Louisa Blair, Bob Chodos, Lorraine Séguin

Page Layout
Interscript

ORIGINAL VERSION

Editorial Manager
Maryse Bérubé

Production Manager
Danielle Latendresse

Coordination Manager
Sylvie Richard

Project Editor
Francine Noël

Copy Editing
Francine Noël, with the assistance
of Christina Jiménez

Proofreading
Francine Noël, Annie Riel, Gabriel Meunier

Picture Research
Carole Régimbald

Cover and Page Layout
Les Studios Artifisme

Maps
Les Studios Artifisme

Illustrations
Monique Chaussé: pages 25, 26, 45, 46, 70, 107, 112, 113, 114, 115, 119
François Girard: page 208
Daniéla Zékina: pages 141, 156

ACKNOWLEDGEMENTS

For having read and provided input on this text during its development, and for their invaluable advice, we wish to warmly thank the following consultants:

ENGLISH VERSION

Pedagogical Consultant:
Tracey Bresee-Morgan
Social Studies Teacher, Massey-Vanier High School
Eastern Townships School Board

ORIGINAL VERSION

Academic Consultant:
Carl Bouchard
Assistant Professor, History Department
Université du Québec à Montréal

Pedagogical Consultants:
Isabelle Bergeron
History Teacher, Collège Bourget
Rigaud

Stéphane Fortier
History Teacher, École secondaire Léopold-Gravel
Commission scolaire des Affluents

Marc Savard
History Teacher, École secondaire Des Sources
Commission scolaire Marguerite-Bourgeoys

My History Log, **Knowledge and Activities – B**

Dépôt légal: 2008
Bibliothèque et Archives nationales du Québec
Bibliothèque et Archives Canada

ISBN 978-2-7617-2721-1

Structure of *My History Log*

My *History Log* is made up of seven chapters (or "inquiries"), which are then subdivided into several sections.

On the Trail

This section allows you to verify what you already know about the social phenomenon you are about to study in the Inquiry.

The brief introduction highlights the general study area, which serves as a background to the Inquiry.

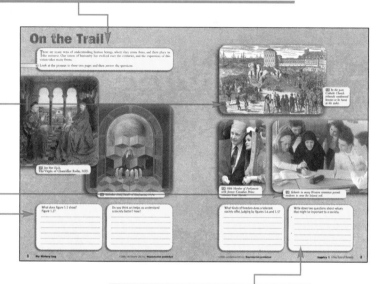

The illustrations show you a common social phenomenon from the present and the past.

The questions ask you to call on what you already know about the social phenomenon being studied. Observe and compare the illustrations: they will help you suggest some answers.

You ask questions that come to mind when you look at the pictures.

At a Glance

This section allows you to discover the historical context in which the social phenomenon was born.

A brief introduction links the text to the previous Inquiry.

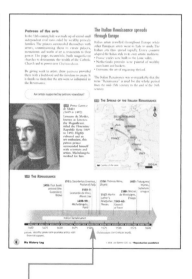

A timeline helps you situate the societies studied in relation to one another. It lists the dates of the major events that will be discussed in the Inquiry.

Project

The project encourages you to be actively involved by giving you the opportunity to engage in historical research and use computer tools.

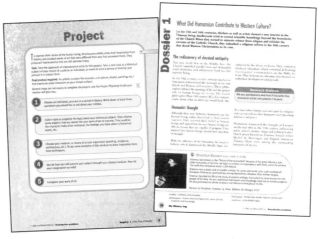

Dossier

Each inquiry has at least two dossiers, which make up its core. The information helps you understand the social phenomenon being studied.

Let's Get to Work!

The activities give you the opportunity to practise what you have learned in the previous sections. We propose various types: short-answer questions, essay-type questions, true-or-false questions, matching questions, tables, graphs, etc.

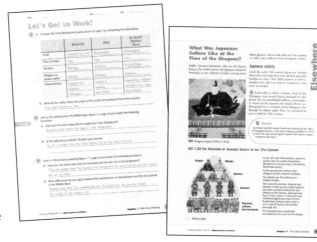

Elsewhere

This section presents one or more societies that existed during the same period as the main society you saw in the dossiers. These societies are studied in the same way as the main society, so you can easily compare them.

Synthesis Activities

The synthesis activities allow you to demonstrate what you have learned throughout the Inquiry and to compare the societies studied. Most of the activities are presented as charts, graphs and tables.

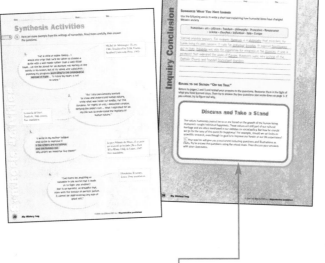

Inquiry Conclusion

At the end of each inquiry, we ask that you write a short summary of what you have learned.

This is also the time for you to review the hypothesis you made in the "On the Trail" section and to answer whatever questions you may have had.

In this section, you must question values inherited from the past and then compare your opinions with those of your classmates. This is an opportunity for you to prepare yourself for the role of citizen.

Inserts

Did you Know ...

This insert provides you with additional information to enrich your knowledge.

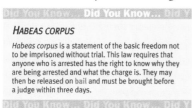

HABEAS CORPUS

Habeas corpus is a statement of the basic freedom not to be imprisoned without trial. This law requires that anyone who is arrested has the right to know why they are being arrested and what the charge is. They may then be released on bail and must be brought before a judge within three days.

Research Mandate

The research mandate is a mini research project on a subject dealt with in *My History Log*.

Research Mandate

Napoleon Bonaparte is a legendary figure in the history of France. Who was he and what did he accomplish? Was he a defender of human rights? Do some research on him to find out.

Notebook

This insert suggests questions that link the present to the past. These questions can be the subject of a classroom discussion.

Do you know what France's motto is today?

Vocabulary

The difficult words (in blue) are defined at the bottom of the page and then listed again in the glossary at the end of the book.

subject: person who is under the authority of a king.

Pictograms

Interdisciplinary links:

  English   Mathematics   Science and Technology   Geography   Art

 Available in Teacher's Copy   Cultural marker

Subject-Specific Competencies

The objective of *My History Log* is to develop the History and Citizenship Education Program's three competencies simultaneously. The sections that aim at a specific competency are identified as follows in the table of contents:

C1 Examines social phenomena from a historical perspective

C2 Interprets social phenomena using the historical method

C3 Constructs his/her consciousness of citizenship through the study of history

Cross-Curricular Competencies

The sections that aim at a specific cross-curricular competency are identified as follows in the table of contents:

CC1 Uses information

CC2 Solves problems

CC3 Exercises critical judgement

CC4 Uses creativity

CC5 Adopts effective work methods

CC6 Uses information and communication technologies

CC7 Achieves his/her potential

CC8 Cooperates with others

CC9 Communicates appropriately

Broad Areas of Learning

The broad areas of learning that provide the context for each inquiry are identified as follows in the table of contents:

AL1 Health and well-being

AL2 Personal and career planning

AL3 Environmental awareness and consumer rights and responsibilities

AL4 Media literacy

AL5 Citizenship and community life

Inquiry 1

Inquiry 2

Inquiry 3

On the Trail

There are many ways of understanding human beings, where they come from, and their place in the universe. Our vision of humanity has evolved over the centuries, and the expression of this vision takes many forms.

A Look at the pictures on these two pages and then answer the questions.

1.1 *Jan Van Eyck,*
The Virgin of Chancellor Rolin, *1435.*

1.2 *Salvador Dalí,* Skull of Zurbarán, *1956.*

What does figure 1.1 show?
Figure 1.2?

_____
_____
_____
_____
_____
_____

Do you think art helps us understand a society better? How?

_____
_____
_____
_____
_____

1.3 *In the past, Catholic Church tribunals condemned heretics to be burnt at the stake.*

1.4 *Sikh Member of Parliament with former Canadian Prime Minister Paul Martin.*

1.5 *Schools in many Western countries permit students to wear the Islamic veil.*

What kinds of freedom does a tolerant society offer, judging by figures 1.4 and 1.5?

_____

_____

_____

_____

_____

Write down two questions about values that might be important to a society.

• _____

_____

• _____

_____

At a Glance

In What Context Did Humanism Evolve?

The 14th century in Europe was marked by famines, wars and epidemics. When the situation began to improve in the 15th century, a change in mentality took place. Fear and a sense of powerlessness gave way to new confidence in the individual. This confidence was expressed in a new trend in art, the Italian Renaissance, and a new trend in thought, humanism.

A The Italian Renaissance

The artistic renewal began in Florence, Italy (see map 1.12 on page 6), in the mid-15th century. Florence was then a prosperous commercial town.

Characteristics of the Italian Renaissance

Artists of the Italian Renaissance were innovative in the following ways:

- They were inspired by the works of ancient Greece and Rome.

- Like the artists of classical antiquity, they wanted to show the beauty of the human body. They looked for harmony in proportion and form, and tried to copy human anatomy accurately. Their works were realistic and they paid special attention to detail.

- The subject matter was new: secular works, particularly portraits, began to appear among the religious works.

- They developed new techniques, such as perspective. Perspective is a technique for representing three dimensions on a flat surface, giving an impression of depth.

Renaissance artists were interested in all forms of artistic expression. They were also curious about everything to do with the human being. Leonardo da Vinci (1452 to 1519) and Michelangelo (1475 to 1564) were two typical Italian Renaissance artists in that they were painters, sculptors and architects all at once. Leonardo da Vinci was also interested in natural sciences and mathematics. He was naturally curious and observant, and invented many machines, including flying machines. They were never built, but his designs reveal a highly inventive mind.

1.6 *Cimabue,* Maestà, *1280.*
This painting from the Middle Ages shows the Virgin Mary surrounded by angels.

1.7 *Titian,* Madonna with the Rabbit, *circa 1530.*

---

secular: not concerned with religion.

✳ **1.9** *Michelangelo*, Pietà, *1498–99.*
The Virgin Mary holds on her lap the body of her son Jesus after his death on the cross. Notice the realism of the clothes and anatomy.

✳ **1.8** *Leonardo da Vinci*, Mona Lisa, *1503–7.*
Mona Lisa is believed to be a portrait of Mona Lisa Gherardini, wife of a rich Florentine merchant. Da Vinci softens the outlines and colour transitions to achieve a hazy effect called *sfumato*. This technique was adopted by other painters of the Italian Renaissance.

MUSIC OF THE RENAISSANCE

✳ Music also reflected an interest in classical antiquity. Italian composer Claudio Monteverdi (1567 to 1643) wrote one of the first operas, *Orfeo* (1607). It tells the story of the Greek demigod Orpheus. Devastated by the death of his wife Eurydice, he is given permission to rescue her from Hades (hell), on condition that he not look back at her on their return. He breaks his promise, and loses Eurydice forever.

dome

columns

1.10 *St. Peter's* Basilica *in Rome, 1506–1605.*

Architects also looked back to classical antiquity. The dome is Romanesque and the columns are in the classical Greek style.

The basilica took 100 years to complete. Imagine the number of artists who worked on it!

Michelangelo was in charge of its construction from 1547, when he became the pope's architect, until his death in 1564. He designed the impressive dome.

St. Peter's Basilica is still the world's largest Christian church.

basilica: title granted by the pope to certain very important churches.

Patrons of the arts

In the 15th century, Italy was made up of several small independent rival states ruled by wealthy princely families. The princes surrounded themselves with artists, commissioning them to create palaces, monuments and works of art as testaments to their power. The pope, meanwhile, built magnificent churches to demonstrate the wealth of the Catholic Church and its power over Christendom.

By giving work to artists, these patrons provided them with a livelihood and the freedom to create. It is thanks to them that the arts were so influential in the Renaissance.

 Are artists supported by patrons nowadays?

1.11 *Prince Lorenzo de Medici (1449 to 1492).*

Lorenzo de Medici, known as Lorenzo the Magnificent, ruled the Florentine Republic from 1469 to 1492. Highly cultured and an art enthusiast, this patron prince surrounded himself with scientists and artists. Michelangelo worked for him.

The Italian Renaissance spreads through Europe

Italian artists travelled throughout Europe, while other European artists went to Italy to study. The Italian arts thus spread rapidly. Every country adapted the Italian style to its own artistic traditions.
• France: castles were built in the Loire valley.
• Netherlands: portraits were painted of wealthy merchants and bankers.
• Germany: the art of engraving thrived.

The Italian Renaissance was so remarkable that the term "Renaissance" is used for the whole period from the mid-15th century to the end of the 16th century.

1.12 THE SPREAD OF THE ITALIAN RENAISSANCE

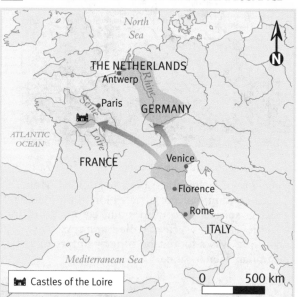

Castles of the Loire

0   500 km

1.13 THE RENAISSANCE

1455: First book printed (the Gutenberg Bible)

1511: Desiderius Erasmus, *Praise of Folly*

1503–7: Leonardo da Vinci, *Mona Lisa*

1498–99: Michelangelo, *Pietà*

1516: Thomas More, *Utopia*

1517: Martin Luther, *Ninety-Five Theses*

1545–63: Council of Trent

1580: Michel de Montaigne, *Essays*

1603: Tokugawa Ieyasu, Japanese shogun

Italian Renaissance

MIDDLE AGES	MIDDLE AGES	MIDDLE AGES	MODERN TIMES	MODERN TIMES	MODERN TIMES	MODERN TIMES	MODERN TIMES	MODERN TIMES	MODERN TIMES
1400	1425	1450	1475	1500	1525	1550	1575	1600	

Christendom: the Christian world.

patron: wealthy person who provides artists with financial support.

Let's Get to Work!

1 a) Compare the three Renaissance works shown on page 5 by completing the table below.

	Mona Lisa	*Pietà*	St. Peter's Basilica, Rome
Artist			
Place of origin			
Art form			
Religious or secular work?			
Characteristics			

b) What do you notice about the origins of the artists who produced these three works?

_____

2 Look at the painting from the Middle Ages (figure 1.6, page 4) and answer the following questions:

a) How does the artist show that the angels are in the background?

_____

_____

b) Is the baby Jesus realistic? Explain your answer.

_____

_____

3 Look at a Renaissance painting (figure 1.7, page 4) and answer the following questions:

a) How does the artist show that the mountains and the man are in the background?

_____

_____

b) What differences do you notice between this painting from the Renaissance and the one painted in the Middle Ages?

_____

_____

4 What are the main characteristics of Renaissance art? Complete the table below.

Characteristics of Renaissance art	
Historical period that inspired the artists	
Subject matter represented in the works	
Example of a new painting technique	
Example of what artists wanted to paint realistically	

A

5 This is a painting of the Roman goddess Venus. List two characteristics that identify it as a work of the Renaissance.

- _____
  _____
  _____

- _____
  _____
  _____

  _____

✳The Birth of Venus, *by Italian painter Sandro Botticelli, circa 1485.*

6 To succeed in their task, Renaissance artists had to acquire knowledge outside the field of art.

a) What knowledge did Michelangelo have to acquire to create the *Pietà* (page 5)?

_____

b) What knowledge do you think he needed to acquire to build St. Peter's Basilica in Rome (page 5)?

_____

_____

7 Name the European country that became famous for each of these artistic techniques during the Renaissance:

ARTISTIC TECHNIQUES	COUNTRY
a) Architecture	_____
b) Painting	_____
c) Engraving	_____

Project

To express their vision of the human being, Renaissance artists drew their inspiration from history and created works of art that were different from any that preceded them. They produced masterpieces that are still admired today.

Task: Take the approach of a Renaissance artist for this project. Take a new look at a historical subject of your choice (it could be an individual, an event or even a period of history) and present it in artistic form.

Final product required: An artistic creation (for example, a sculpture, model, painting, etc.) that expresses your viewpoint on your chosen subject.

Several steps are necessary to complete the project. Use the Project Planning Guide TC that your teacher will give you.

1 Choose an individual, an event or a period in history. Write down at least three questions you would like to ask about your subject.

2 Collect data to establish the facts about your historical subject. Then choose some aspects that you would like your work of art to express. This could be the character traits of an individual, the feelings you have about a historical event, etc.

3 Choose your medium, or means of artistic expression (painting, sculpture, architecture, etc.). Study some examples of this medium to draw inspiration from the techniques used.

4 Decide how you will present your subject through your chosen medium. Now let your imagination run wild!

5 Complete your work of art.

What Did Humanism Contribute to Western Culture?

In the 15th and 16th centuries, thinkers as well as artists showed a new interest in the human being. Intellectuals tried to extend scientific knowledge beyond the restrictions of the Church. When they started to separate science from religion and criticize the excesses of the Catholic Church, they unleashed a religious reform in the 16th century that shook Western Christendom to its core.

The rediscovery of classical antiquity

You may recall that in the Middle Ages the Church controlled people's lives and demanded total obedience and submission. God was the supreme being.

In the 15th century, erudite scholars known as humanists rediscovered the writings of ancient Greek and Roman philosophers. These philosophers debated the meaning of life and the proper role of human beings in society. The Greek philosopher Plato (4th century BC), for example, wrote about what an ideal city would look like.

replaced by the desire to know. They criticized medieval education, which consisted of learning theologians' commentaries on the Bible by heart. They believed in education that focused on individual development and growth.

> ### Research Mandate
> Ask your grandparents what kind of education they received at school, and compare it to yours.

Humanist thought

Although they were believers, humanists saw the human being, rather than God, as their central concern. They asserted their belief in human beings, and argued that because human beings are able to reason, they are capable of progress. They insisted that human beings should have freedom of thought.

With the influence of the humanists, the need to believe, which dominated the Middle Ages, was

At a time when Europe was torn apart by religious wars, as you will see later, humanists were preaching tolerance and peace.

Humanism dominated the thought of Europe's intellectual elite in the 16th century, influencing artists, princes, writers, clergy and political leaders. Dutch priest Desiderius Erasmus, French writer Michel de Montaigne and English statesman Thomas More were among the outstanding humanists of the era.

✷ DESIDERIUS ERASMUS (CIRCA 1469 TO 1536)

Erasmus was known as the "Prince of the Humanists" because of his great influence over other humanists of his time. He kept up a lively correspondence with them, which he printed. The collection contained about 1,200 letters!

Erasmus was a priest and an erudite scholar. He spoke and wrote Latin. Latin enabled all European thinkers to communicate among themselves, whatever their mother tongue.

Erasmus devoted his life to the study of ancient writings, from which he drew lessons for the people of his time. He was convinced that reason and knowledge were key to human progress. He also promoted the ideals of peace and tolerance throughout his life.

Portrait of Desiderius Erasmus by Hans Holbein the Younger, 1523.

---

erudite: scholarly, well-educated.

philosopher: thinker who investigates the nature of truth, existence and knowledge.

medieval: of the Middle Ages.

theologian: thinker who studies God and divine truth.

clergy: the body of people who exercise religious ministry.

✷ MICHEL DE MONTAIGNE (1533 TO 1592)

In his *Essays*, Montaigne wrote about himself very frankly, which was quite new at the time. He also rejected all certainties, and advocated doubt, criticism and freedom of thought.

Like Erasmus, he declared his horror of war and advocated tolerance. He made many trips throughout Europe, and his observations of different laws and customs led him to believe in cultural tolerance.

Although he spoke and wrote Latin, Montaigne wrote his *Essays* in French to make them accessible to more people. His *Essays* were very popular among his contemporaries.

Portrait of Michel de Montaigne. Anonymous, 16th century.

Research Mandate

Do some research on a Renaissance writer who wrote in his mother tongue rather than in Latin. For example, William Shakespeare (England), Miguel de Cervantes (Spain), François Rabelais (France).

✷ THOMAS MORE (1478 TO 1535)

Thomas More, a great friend of Erasmus, was the most important English humanist. After studying law he pursued a brilliant political career.

In his major work, *Utopia* (1516), he imagined an ideal world where peace and tolerance reigned. The word "utopia" has entered the language as a noun, meaning an idealistic but impractical imagined society. More's *Utopia* was popular throughout Europe.

Portrait of Thomas More by Peter Paul Rubens, 16th century.

Humanism can be summed up as follows:

1.14 HUMANISM

Humanists
Artists, princes, writers, priests, etc.

Question
What is the place of the human being in the world?

Inspiration
Ancient Greek and Roman philosophers

New philosophy

- Confidence in reason and progress
- Need to know
- Tolerance and peace

- Doubt and criticism of certitudes
- Demand for freedom of thought
- Education aimed at individual growth

---

advocate: to speak or write in favour of a cause.

The spread of humanism

As you can see in this map, humanist ideas spread throughout western Europe. How did this happen? Many factors explain the phenomenon:

– the many trips taken by humanists throughout Europe;

– the letters they wrote to one another;

– the development of European towns and universities, where they met and exchanged ideas;

– a technical revolution: printing.

1.15 CENTRES OF HUMANISM IN THE 15TH AND 16TH CENTURIES

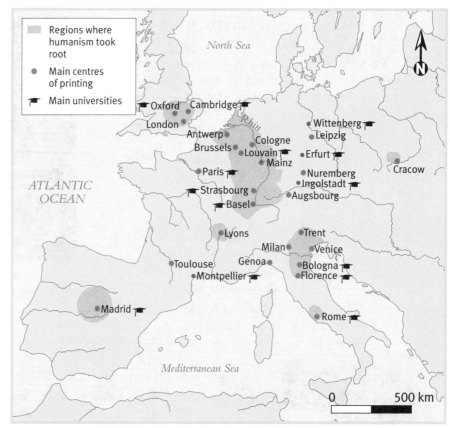

Legend:
- Regions where humanism took root
- Main centres of printing
- Main universities

North Sea
Oxford, Cambridge, London, Antwerp, Brussels, Cologne, Louvain, Mainz, Paris, Erfurt, Nuremberg, Ingolstadt, Strasbourg, Augsbourg, Basel, Wittenberg, Leipzig, Cracow
ATLANTIC OCEAN
Lyons, Milan, Trent, Venice, Genoa, Bologna, Florence, Toulouse, Montpellier, Madrid, Rome
Mediterranean Sea

0 500 km

A print shop in the 15th century.

PRINTING

Printing was invented in China in the 11th century. The Chinese used movable wooden type (blocks with raised letters) to reproduce texts. This process was unknown to Europeans, who copied out books by hand.

✴ Born in Mainz, metalworker Johannes Gutenberg had the idea of making movable type out of metal in about 1450. He also invented a printing press. In 1455, he printed the first book, a Bible.

Between 1455 and 1500, about 35,000 books were published, with a total of 15 to 20 million copies going into circulation. By about 1500, more than 200 European towns had printing presses.

More than two thirds of the books were in Latin, and nearly half were religious in nature (Bibles, prayer books, etc.). The rest were by ancient Greek and Latin writers and by humanists.

 During the Renaissance, the printing press enabled ideas to spread far and wide. What means of communication play the same role today?

Let's Get to Work!

1 a) Separate the following characteristics according to whether they belong to medieval or humanist thought.

> the human being as the main concern • obedience • freedom • happiness • submission • feeling of powerlessness • tolerance • God as the main concern

Medieval	Humanist
_____	_____
_____	_____
_____	_____

b) In keeping with your answers to part a), would you say the values of today's society are a legacy of medieval or of humanist thought?

_____

2 a) Explain in your own words what tolerance is.

_____

_____

b) Would you say the society in which you live applies this humanist value? Give reasons for your answer.

_____

_____

3 a) In what language did humanists correspond? Why?

_____

_____

b) Do you remember when Europeans began using this language?

_____

c) Do you think everybody spoke this language? Explain your answer.

_____

_____

_____

d) What language is used for international exchange today?

_____

e) What other languages do you speak?

_____

Inquiry 1 A New Vision of Humanity **13**

4 a) Study map 1.15 on page 12, and name two means by which humanist thought spread throughout Europe.

_____

b) How are ideas spread today?

_____

_____

5 a) Before the invention of printing, books were copied by hand by monks in monasteries. Do the following statements apply to monastic scribes, printers or both?

	MONASTIC SCRIBES	PRINTERS
1. They reproduced texts by hand.	◯	◯
2. They reproduced texts with a press.	◯	◯
3. They reproduced religious texts, such as the Bible.	◯	◯
4. They reproduced texts by humanists and thinkers of classical antiquity.	◯	◯
5. They worked very slowly.	◯	◯
6. They worked fast.	◯	◯

b) Printed books cost 20 to 50 times less than copied manuscripts. Why?

_____

_____

6 a) From where did humanists draw their inspiration and their knowledge?

_____

b) How does that make them similar to Renaissance artists?

_____

7 Complete the following sentences.

a) In the Middle Ages, education consisted of _____

_____

b) For humanists, education should be about _____

_____

8 Give your own definition of humanism.

_____

_____

_____

9 Read these newspaper headlines and identify the humanist idea they refer to using the terms below.

> peace • freedom of thought • the need to know • doubt • tolerance •
> education aimed at the growth of the individual

a) **Researcher questions effectiveness of medication**

b) **QUEBECERS OPPOSE MILITARY INTERVENTION IN IRAQ**

c) **Quebec courtrooms allow oaths on the Bible or on one's honour**

d) **RESULTS OF MEDICAL STUDY AVAILABLE ON THE INTERNET**

e) **School principal permits all religious symbols**

f) **School hires specialists to help children with learning disabilities**

Scientific progress during the Renaissance

You may remember that in the Middle Ages the Church had a stranglehold on science. Among other things, it taught that the earth was flat and located at the centre of the universe. It forbade, on pain of death, any new idea that it considered in conflict with biblical texts.

Scientific progress was a result of the humanists' interest in the human being, their criticism of accepted beliefs and their recognition that doubt and observation were important sources of knowledge. This progress continued beyond the Renaissance.

Research Mandate

Choose a Renaissance scientist, such as Ambroise Paré, Michel Servet, Nicolaus Copernicus, Paracelsus, Andreas Vesalius or Galileo, and find out what he did to advance scientific knowledge.

By dissecting corpses, a practice forbidden by the Church, scientists learned more about human anatomy, which led to advances in medicine. Remarkable advances were made in medicine, mathematics and physics, but also in astronomy and geography, as you will see in Inquiry 2. In particular, scientists invented many instruments for observing and measuring that made even more discoveries possible.

Study the table below listing some of the inventions and discoveries of the 16th and 17th centuries.

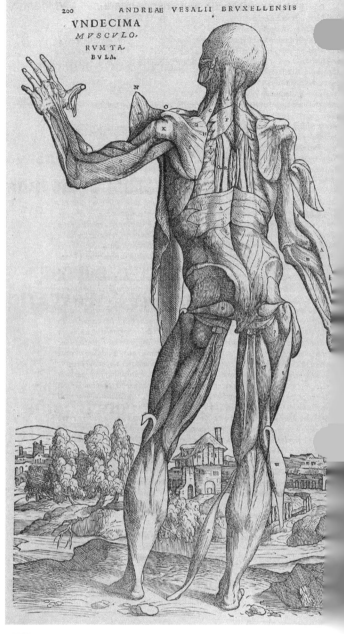

1.16 *The muscular structure. Engraving published in Andreas Vesalius' treatise on anatomy* De corporis humani fabrica, *1543.*

SOME INVENTIONS AND DISCOVERIES OF THE 16TH AND 17TH CENTURIES

Medicine	Mathematics	Instruments	
		Observation	Measurement
• Invention of concave lenses for myopia (1440)	• + and – signs (about 1490)	• Microscope (1604)	• Thermometer (1593)
	• Square root (about 1525)	• Refracting telescope (1610)	
• Discovery of blood circulation (about 1543)			• Calculator (1642)
	• = sign (1557)	• Reflecting telescope (1668)	• Barometer (1643)
• Discovery of pulmonary circulation (1553)			

Let's Get to Work!

1 a) Complete the following diagram to show how humanist ideas contributed to the development of science during the Renaissance.

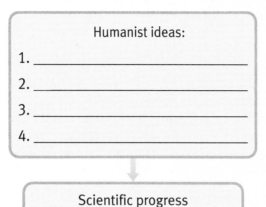

Humanist ideas:

1. _____
2. _____
3. _____
4. _____

Scientific progress

b) Do these ideas still motivate today's scientists? Give one example.

_____

_____

2 Renaissance inventions and discoveries have had lasting repercussions.
For each of the inventions and discoveries listed below, name an application found in society today.

Renaissance inventions and discoveries	Application today
Discovery of blood circulation and pulmonary circulation	Better treatment of heart and lung disease.
Invention of the barometer	
Invention of the microscope	
Invention of the telescope	
Invention of the calculator	

3 What group in society do you think opposed the progress of science during the Renaissance? Why?

_____

_____

How Did Humanism Change Christendom?

Humanist values, such as freedom of thought and the desire for knowledge, inspired a protest movement in the early 16th century that ended up dividing Christians of the West.

The Reformation

The Reformation was a movement that began as an attempt to **reform** the Roman Catholic Church and led to the founding of new branches of the Christian religion: the Protestant churches.

Criticism of the Church

Since the Middle Ages, the Church had been going through a major internal crisis. Members of the clergy were not honouring their vows of poverty and **chastity**. The pope and the bishops behaved like powerful noblemen and lived in luxury. Parish priests were ignorant, neglected their parishioners and were unsupervised by their bishops.

✳ In the early 15th century some members of the clergy, including Cardinal Nicholas of Cusa (1401 to 1464), began to call for a reform of the Church. In 1511, Erasmus published *Praise of Folly*, in which he criticized the excesses of the clergy. The humanists also wanted the **Bible** to be translated into local languages to make it accessible to everyone. At the time, the only Bibles were in Latin, a language that ordinary people did not speak.

The birth of Protestantism

In 1517, Pope Leo X began to sell **indulgences** to finance the building of St. Peter's Basilica in Rome. Access to heaven thus became a question of money. A German monk named Martin Luther denounced this practice and other injustices in the Catholic Church in his Ninety-Five **Theses** addressed to the pope. He proclaimed that all baptized Christians were equal and did not need the Church's supervision.

> "Christians are to be taught that he who gives to the poor or lends to the needy does a better work than buying pardons ... Why does not the pope, whose wealth is today greater than the riches of the richest, build just this one church of St. Peter with his own money, rather than with the money of poor believers? ... The indulgences which the preachers cry as the 'greatest graces' are known to be truly such, in so far as they promote gain..."

Excerpts from Martin Luther's Ninety-Five Theses, 1517. From *Works of Martin Luther*, edited by H.E. Jacobs and A. Spaeth. Philadelphia: A. J. Holman Company, 1915.

✳ **MARTIN LUTHER (1483 TO 1546)**

A German humanist, Luther studied law at the University of Erfurt, in Germany. Soon afterwards he suffered a serious personal crisis: he was terrified of death and divine judgement and despaired of avoiding them. He dropped out of school, became a monk, and studied and taught theology at Erfurt.

Studying the New Testament convinced Luther that faith alone was enough to admit people to heaven. He believed that all Christians were equal, and that all should be able to read the Bible for themselves, which would nourish their faith. He translated the Bible into German and printed 100,000 copies.

Portrait of Luther by Lucas Cranach the Elder, 1541.

---

reform: profound change in an institution with a view to improving it.

chastity: abstinence from all sexual intercourse.

Bible: sacred book of Christianity made up of the Old and New Testaments.

indulgence: access to heaven granted to the faithful by the pope in return for a donation to the Church.

thesis: position that a person is committed to defending in public.

The pope rejected Luther's Ninety-Five Theses and **excommunicated** him. Luther asked Erasmus to support him against the Church, but Erasmus refused for the sake of keeping Christians united. Luther was encouraged by German princes united in opposition against their emperor, Charles V, who remained loyal to the pope. Luther thus found himself at the head of a new church, the Lutheran Church. Lutheranism enjoyed immediate success in Germany, and spread through northern Europe (Sweden, Denmark, Norway) and Switzerland. Luther worked at organizing the new church and defining its major principles.

In the same period, two other churches similar to the Lutheran Church came into being: the Calvinist and Anglican churches.

"Protestants" was the name given to followers of these new branches of the Christian religion born of the Reformation. Christians who remained faithful to the pope took the name "Catholics."

1.17 *Martin Luther publicly burns the pope's document excommunicating him.*

✳ **1.18** *John Calvin (1509 to 1564), founder of Calvinism. Anonymous painting, 16th century.*

Influenced by humanist ideas, Calvin thought knowledge about the human being was as important as knowledge of God. He believed people should work hard and use their God-given power of reason. Calvinists saw personal wealth as a sign of God's favour, which explained the success of Calvinism among the middle classes. Calvinism spread mainly to France, Switzerland and northern Europe.

1.19 *King Henry VIII (1491 to 1547), founder of the Anglican Church. Painting by Hans Holbein the Younger, 1536.*

In 1534, the king of England, Henry VIII, who had reigned since 1509, stopped recognizing the authority of the pope because he refused to annul the king's marriage to Catherine of Aragon. Henry then founded the Anglican Church and became its leader. Thomas More, who opposed this plan, was beheaded by order of the king in 1535.

---

excommunicate: expel from the Church.

annul: declare a marriage invalid.

MAIN DIFFERENCES BETWEEN CATHOLICS AND PROTESTANTS IN THE 16TH CENTURY

	Catholics	Protestants
Worship	• They prayed to God, the Virgin Mary, the saints and Jesus Christ.	• They prayed to God and Jesus only. There was no devotion to the Virgin Mary and the saints.
Salvation (access to heaven)	• By faith and works (alms, donations to the Church, pilgrimages, etc.).	• By faith only.
Organization	• Hierarchy (pope, bishops, priests). • Clergy could not marry.	• Equality. • Ministers could marry.
Bible	• The Bible was in Latin, so only the clergy could read it. • Only theologians could interpret the Bible.	• The Bible was translated into the language of ordinary church members. • All Christians were encouraged to read and interpret the Bible.
Sacraments	• There were seven sacraments: baptism, confirmation, the Eucharist, marriage, extreme unction, ordination, penance.	• There were only two sacraments: baptism and communion.
Religious services	• In a church, which was often lavish.	• In a simple building.

The Counter-Reformation

In spite of the criticism directed at it since the Middle Ages, the Church had not managed to reform itself from the inside. The success of Protestantism finally convinced the Church that reform was necessary.

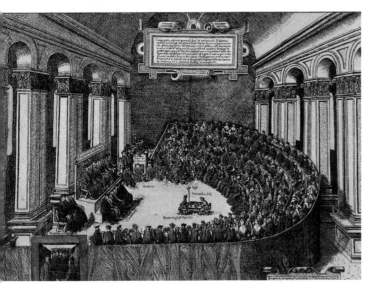

1.20 *The Council of Trent, 1545–63.*

> Are there changes you would like to see in the religion you practise? If so, what are they?

The Council of Trent

In 1545, Pope Paul III assembled a **council** in the city of Trent, Italy, to discuss with the bishops and Catholic sovereigns of Europe how to react to the Reformation. The Council of Trent lasted 18 years, with the following results:

• Bishops and priests had to live in their dioceses and supervise the parish priests.

• Colleges were founded to educate priests.

• An official version of the Bible in Latin was produced.

• The Inquisition (a religious tribunal established in the 13th century to prosecute **heretics**) was strengthened so that it could seek out, bring to trial and sentence to death all those who opposed the Catholic faith.

• New religious orders were founded, in particular the Ursulines, Capuchins and Jesuits, whose mission was to teach and spread the Roman Catholic faith.

council: assembly convened by the pope to make major decisions concerning the Church.

heretic: person who holds an opinion contrary to the established beliefs of the Church.

The effects of the Counter-Reformation

With the Council of Trent, the pope hoped to reunite all Christians within the Church by making a number of reforms that had long been called for. But far from reuniting the churches, the Council of Trent marked the final separation of the Roman Catholic from the Protestant churches.

On the other hand, one of the effects of the Council of Trent was to revive enthusiasm for the Roman Catholic Church. The religious passion of the Jesuits was especially outstanding. Highly educated, they preached far and wide. They successfully challenged Protestant preachers, founded colleges and were close advisors to Roman Catholic monarchs.

The Counter-Reformation curbed the expansion of Protestantism in Europe, and in many places forced its retreat.

The division of Christendom

Christianity had suffered its first division in the 11th century. In 1054, Eastern Christians had split with Western Christians to form the Orthodox Church.

In the 16th century, after the Reformation, Christian Europe found itself divided into three groups: Orthodox, Roman Catholic and Protestant.

The spread of Protestant churches caused violent confrontations in many parts of Europe. In the Holy Roman Empire (Germany), the Roman Catholic Emperor Charles V declared war on those of his princes who had converted to Protestant faiths. One of the bloodiest wars was the Thirty Years' War (1618–48). Beginning in Germany, it gradually spread to much of Europe. It is estimated that Germany lost between 30% and 50% of its population during that war!

The map below shows the religious divisions in Europe at the time the religious wars ended.

Research Mandate

France was also torn apart by wars of religion. Find out about the St. Bartholomew's Day Massacre in 1572, when Catholics killed more than 3,000 Protestants in Paris.

1.21 RELIGIOUS DIVISIONS IN EUROPE IN THE MID-17TH CENTURY

Are there other countries where Protestantism is practised today? Catholicism? Name those you know.

Do you remember what Muslims believe?

Name: .... Group: .... Date: ....

Let's Get to Work!

1 What were the three main criticisms of the Roman Catholic Church? What happened as a result of these criticisms? To answer, fill in the following diagram:

Criticisms of the Roman Catholic Church

1. ____________ 2. ____________ 3. ____________

Consequence

____

2 Martin Luther encouraged all believers to read the Bible.

a) What did he do to make the Bible accessible?

____

b) What invention enabled him to distribute the Bible to Christians?

____

3 Humanists Martin Luther, John Calvin, Henry VIII, Desiderius Erasmus and Thomas More criticized the Catholic Church. To whom does each of the following statements apply?

a) He founded a new church because of a personal conflict with the pope.

____

b) He founded a new church that spread to France, Switzerland and beyond.

____

c) He was excommunicated after publishing 95 theses criticizing the Catholic Church.

____

d) The king of England ordered him beheaded for refusing to recognize him as leader of the Church.

____

e) They wanted Christendom to remain united.

____

4 Name one way in which Protestant ministers differ from Catholic priests.

____

Let's Get to Work!

5 Martin Luther criticized the wealth of the Church and the fact that people were not allowed to read the Bible for themselves. What current of thought did these criticisms come from?

_____

6 Which of these statements refer to Protestant churches? Check the correct answers.

○ The Bible is their sacred book.

○ They recognize the pope's authority.

○ They worship in their mother tongue.

○ They celebrate seven sacraments.

○ They reject devotion to the saints and the Virgin Mary.

7 St. Paul's writings contained in the Bible (first century AD) greatly inspired Martin Luther. Read this excerpt and then answer the questions.

> "For our argument is that a man is justified by faith quite apart from success in keeping the law ... And for every well-doer there will be glory, honour and peace ... For God has no favourites ... There is no distinction between Jew and Greek, because the same Lord is Lord of all, and is rich enough for the need of all who invoke him."
>
> St. Paul, from the Letter of Paul to the Romans, *The New English Bible,* Oxford University Press, 1961

a) Find a synonym for "faith" in a dictionary.

_____

b) Which law is St. Paul speaking about? Check the correct answer.

○ The law of the king

○ The law of nature

○ Religious law

c) Highlight a passage from the excerpt that may have convinced Luther that all Christians are equal.

_____

d) Using the excerpt above and the table on page 20, list at least three characteristics of Protestantism.

- _____

- _____

- _____

8 a) How did the Church react to Martin Luther's criticisms?

_____

b) What was the general attitude of the Church towards its critics in the 16th century? Check the correct answer.

◯ The Church agreed to dialogue with its critics.

◯ The Church did not tolerate any criticism.

◯ The Church agreed to change as soon as it was criticized.

9 Have a look at map 1.21 on page 21. Which groups mentioned are Christian and which are non-Christian? Fill in the table below and then highlight groups that arose in the Renaissance.

Christians	Non-Christians

10 In 1598, in an attempt to end the wars of religion in France, King Henry IV signed the Edict of Nantes. Here is an excerpt:

> "We have permitted, and herewith permit, those of the said religion called Reformed to live and abide in all the cities and places of this our kingdom and countries of our sway, without being annoyed, molested, or compelled to do anything in the matter of religion contrary to their consciences ... We also permit those of the said religion to make and continue the exercise of the same in all villages and places of our dominion where it was established by them and publicly enjoyed ... We also forbid all our subjects, of whatever quality and condition, from carrying off by force or persuasion, against the will of their parents, the children of the said religion, in order to cause them to be baptized or confirmed in the Catholic Apostolic and Roman Church."
>
> Edict of Nantes, 1598. From *Readings in European History,* edited by J.H. Robinson. Boston: Ginn, 1906.

a) What are the rights of Protestants that this edict recognized? Find four.

- _____

- _____

- _____

- _____

b) Highlight passages that suggest the difficulties Protestants must have experienced before the Edict of Nantes.

11 Explain in your own words how humanism changed Christendom in Europe.

_____

_____

_____

_____

What Was Japanese Culture Like at the Time of the Shoguns?

Unlike European humanists, who saw the human being as the central concern, the Japanese considered humanity as one element of nature among many others. Japanese culture in the 16th and 17th centuries was thus quite different from European culture.

Japanese society

Until the early 17th century, Japan was divided into many rival states that were ruled by powerful families, or clans. Clan chiefs, known as *daimios*, fought one another to achieve dominance, but none succeeded.

✳ Eventually in 1603, a daimio named Ieyasu who was chief of the Tokugawa clan managed to take power. He was proclaimed military commander, or *shogun*, by the emperor, the *mikado*. Power was then passed on to members of the Tokugawa clan through hereditary rights. This clan remained in power until the 19th century.

1.22 *Tokugawa Ieyasu (1542 to 1616).*

> ✳ **SHOGUN**
>
> Australian novelist James Clavell was inspired by the story of Tokugawa Ieyasu. In his novel *Shogun*, published in 1975, he tells the story of an English explorer who lived in Japan during the clan wars.

1.23 THE STRUCTURE OF JAPANESE SOCIETY IN THE 17TH CENTURY

Shogun

Mikado

Daimios

Samurai

Peasants, artisans and merchants

Military roles

In the 16th and 17th centuries, Japanese society was thoroughly hierarchical. Because of continuous wars, the military dominated society.

At the top were the military chief (shogun) and the emperor (mikado).

The mikado was the political and religious leader.

Then came the daimios. Daimios had warriors in their service, called samurai, who were trained to defend the vast domains of the daimios. Samurai were loyal to their masters in the same way medieval knights were loyal to their feudal lords. Samurai were under a strict code of honour, the bushido (see page 26).

The population was completely dominated by the power of the military.

THE 武士道*, THE SAMURAI CODE OF HONOUR

The main virtue of a samurai was his sense of honour. In battle, he had to show self-control and courage. He led a frugal life. One of his weapons was a Shinto sabre, a sacred sword symbolizing the soul, the loyalty, the spirit of sacrifice and the courage of the samurai.

A samurai's life belonged so completely to his master that if his master died, the samurai could choose *seppuku*, a complicated form of ritual suicide. Samurai preferred suicide to dishonour.

✳ *Shinto sabre.*

★ *bushido* in Japanese

1.24 JAPAN IN THE 17TH CENTURY

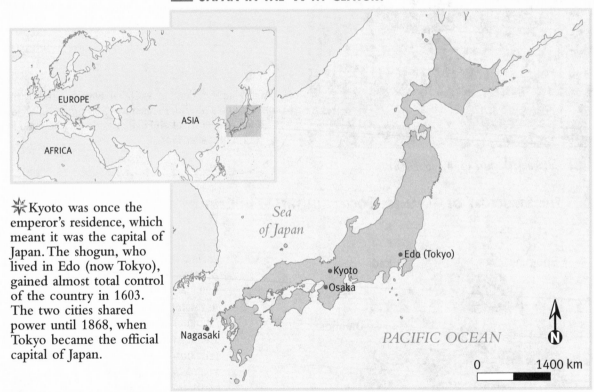

✳ Kyoto was once the emperor's residence, which meant it was the capital of Japan. The shogun, who lived in Edo (now Tokyo), gained almost total control of the country in 1603. The two cities shared power until 1868, when Tokyo became the official capital of Japan.

Before the 17th century, Japan had ties with China and several European countries including Spain, Portugal and the Netherlands. These European countries traded with Japan and established Christian missions there to evangelize the Japanese. But the successive shoguns of the Tokugawa clan, wishing to preserve Japanese identity, closed Japan to outside influences, Chinese as well as European. From the reign of Tokugawa Ieyasu onwards, Japanese converts to Christianity were persecuted and most Europeans were expelled from the country. Japan thus cut itself off from the outside world for more than two centuries.

---

frugal: simple, plain, not lavish.

Japanese religion

The Japanese believed the visible world co-existed with another world, invisible and supernatural. This belief gave rise to a **polytheistic** religion called Shintoism. Its divinities, the *kami*, are invisible spirits that can be good or evil. Shintoism is animist: the gods can dwell within powerful elements of nature, such as a fox, a stag or a waterfall. The Japanese celebrate nature by performing religious rituals such as the rice ceremony or the water feast. Shintoism has strongly influenced Japanese culture, particularly the arts.

Japanese art

Japanese art took many forms.

- **Landscaping:** Gardens generally included a pond, trees, flowers and carefully arranged stones. How these features were laid out had **spiritual** significance.

1.26 *Torii.*

These big red porticos, or *torii*, are symbolic gateways between the two worlds of Shintoism: the real, visible world and the divine, invisible world. They are often found at the entrance to Shinto temples.

1.25 *Nature scene by the Japanese painter Sotatsu, early 17th century.*

- **Architecture:** Japanese buildings blended in with nature. They were usually wooden. A terrace at the front symbolized the passage between the social and the intimate.

- **Painting:** Japanese painters often depicted human activities or nature scenes.

- ✷ **Theatre:** Japan developed a very distinctive form of theatre called Noh. Noh plays are sacred and tragic, there is no scenery and the actors, all men, wear masks. Noh theatre creates an atmosphere of strangeness and gives spectators the feeling of being in a magical universe, at the border between the visible world and the invisible.

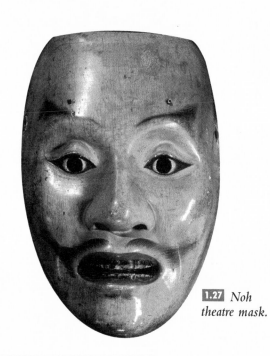

1.27 *Noh theatre mask.*

---

polytheist: someone who worships many gods.

spiritual: to do with the spirit or soul.

Let's Get to Work!

1 Match each of the statements below to the relevant Japanese social group.

a) We have no personal power and must serve our masters.

_____

b) I am the spiritual leader of Japan.

_____

c) In fact, I exercise the real power.

_____

d) I am a warrior under the rule of my lord.

_____

e) I am a military chief and member of a clan.

_____

2 a) What kind of connections did Europe and Japan have in the 16th century?

_____

b) Who disrupted these connections in the 17th century?

_____

c) Why were these ties broken?

_____

_____

3 Name one way in which samurai demonstrated loyalty to their masters.

_____

4 What values were important to warriors in Japanese society?

_____

_____

5 Do you get the impression that the Japanese were critical of authority in the 17th century? Explain your answer.

_____

_____

_____

6 Which of the following values do you think are associated with humanism, and which with the Japan of the shoguns?

	HUMANISM	JAPAN OF THE SHOGUNS
a) Freedom	○	○
b) Fidelity	○	○
c) A sense of honour	○	○
d) The spirit of sacrifice	○	○

7 Explain how each of the following forms of artistic expression was related to religion in the Japan of the shoguns.

a) Painting: _____

_____

b) Landscaping: _____

_____

c) Architecture: _____

_____

d) Noh theatre: _____

_____

8 Were Renaissance artists in Europe also inspired by their religion? Give a specific example.

_____

_____

9 Name a difference between Christianity and Shintoism.

_____

_____

_____

10 Indicate beside each statement below whether it corresponds to the Shinto or the humanist perspective on the human being.

a) The human being is the central concern: _____

b) The human being is one element of nature among others: _____

Synthesis Activities

E

1 Here are some excerpts from the writings of humanists. Read them carefully, then answer the questions.

Michel de Montaigne, *Essays,* 1580. Translated by D.M. Frame. Stanford University Press, 1965

1.

"For a child of noble family ... I would also urge that care be taken to choose a guide with a well-made rather than a well-filled head ... Let him be asked for an account not merely of the words of his lesson, but of its sense and substance ... planning his progress according to the pedagogical method of Plato ... To know by heart is not to know."

2.

"But I also passionately wanted to know and understand human nature, know what was inside our bodies. For this purpose, for nights on end, I dissected corpses, defying the pope's ban ... What I searched for all my life was to understand the mystery of human nature."

Leonardo da Vinci, *Notebooks,* 16th century. Free translation.

3.

"I write in my mother tongue
And strive to improve it
If the Greeks are so famous
And the Romans too
Why aren't we immortal like them?"

Jacques Peletier du Mans, *À un poè qui n'écrivait qu'en latin,* (To a Poet Who Wrote Only in Latin), 1547. Free translation.

4.

"Can there be anything so valuable in the world that it leads us to fight one another? War is so harmful, so dreadful that, even with the excuse of perfect justice, it cannot be approved by any man of good will."

Desiderius Erasmus, *Letters.* Free translatio

a) Highlight the passages in the previous excerpts that show the humanists' admiration for classical antiquity.

b) Name three mother tongues spoken at the time of Peletier du Mans (excerpt no. 3).

_____

c) In his *Essays* Montaigne uses the following expressions (excerpt no. 1). Indicate whether he was referring to medieval education or to humanist education.

	MIDDLE AGES	HUMANISM
1. "a well-made [head]"	○	○
2. "a well-filled head"	○	○
3. "[Ask him to repeat] the words of his lesson"	○	○
4. "[Ask him about] its sense and substance"	○	○
5. "To know by heart"	○	○

d) Would you say the teaching you receive is inspired by medieval education or by humanist education? Explain your answer

_____

_____

e) Explain in your own words the main idea contained in each excerpt.

Excerpt	Main idea
1. Michel de Montaigne	_____ _____
2. Leonardo da Vinci	_____ _____
3. Jacques Peletier du Mans	_____ _____
4. Desiderius Erasmus	_____ _____

2) The number of printing presses increased rapidly in Europe in the 15th and 16th centuries.

a) Explain in your own words how printing contributed to the spread of knowledge, and still does today.

_____

_____

b) Complete the following sentences.

Printed books can be produced more _____ than handwritten books.

_____ books are cheaper than _____ books.

(3) a) Imagine you are the religious reformer Martin Luther and write to the pope to express your criticisms.

_____

_____

_____

_____

_____

_____

_____

_____

_____

b) Now imagine you are the pope and answer Martin Luther's criticisms.

_____

_____

_____

_____

_____

_____

_____

_____

_____

(4) Considering the Reformation and the Counter-Reformation, would you say humanism was a force for unity or division in Europe in the 16th and 17th centuries? Give reasons for your answer.

_____

_____

_____

_____

(5) Among the following groups, identify those that helped develop humanist philosophy.

◯ Priests   ◯ Farmers

◯ Writers   ◯ Soldiers

◯ Artisans   ◯ Princes

◯ Artists   ◯ Intellectuals

Synthesis Activities

6 Fill in this page summarizing what you have learned in this Inquiry.

The humanist movement in Europe during the Renaissance

Era: _____

Main focus of concern: _____

Artistic movement

    Name: _____

    Origin: _____

    Two representatives: _____

    Characteristics: _____

    _____

Humanist ideas

    Science: _____

    Religion: _____

    _____

    Education: _____

    _____

    Human values: _____

Religious movement growing out of humanism: _____

How humanism was communicated: _____

_____

Humanist legacy: _____

_____

_____

Name: .... Group: .... Date: ....

SUMMARIZE WHAT YOU HAVE LEARNED

Use the following words to write a short text explaining how humanist ideas have changed Western society.

> humanism • art • criticism • freedom • philosophy • Protestant • Renaissance • science • churches • individual • Italy • Europe

_____

_____

_____

_____

_____

_____

_____

_____

RETURN TO THE SECTION "ON THE TRAIL"

Return to pages 2 and 3 and reread your answers to the questions. Reassess them in the light of what you have learned since. Then try to answer the two questions you wrote down on page 3. If you cannot, try to figure out why.

Discuss and Take a Stand

The values humanists passed on to us are based on the growth of the human being. Humanists sought individual happiness. These values are still part of our cultural heritage and are often mentioned in our debates on social policy. But how far should we go for the sake of this quest for happiness? For example, should we set limits on scientific research, even though its goal is to improve our health or our life expectancy?

TC Your teacher will give you a worksheet including questions and illustrations as clues. Try to answer the questions using the visual clues. Then discuss your answers with your classmates.

On the Trail

Many of your possessions were made neither in Quebec nor in Canada, but in other countries, some of them very far away. Many of these countries produce goods to satisfy the demand in rich countries. This kind of economic relationship between countries began in the Renaissance, in the 16th century, when European explorers set out to discover the world.

Look at the illustrations on these two pages and then answer the questions.

2.1 *Americans walking on the moon, July 21, 1969.*

2.2 *Christopher Columbus arriving in America, October 12, 1492.*

Why did countries send out explorers to discover new lands?

_____

_____

_____

_____

_____

When people of different cultures meet, what can happen?

_____

_____

_____

_____

_____

2.3 *Children sewing soccer balls in a factory in Pakistan.*

2.4 *Women working in a garment factory in Ecuador.*

2.5 *Black slaves working in a cotton plantation in 19th-century North America.*

Do people of different cultures sometimes exploit one another? Give examples.

_____
_____
_____
_____
_____
_____

Write down two questions that come to mind when you look at the pictures on these two pages.

• _____
  _____

• _____
  _____

At a Glance

In What Context Did Explorers Set Out to Discover the World?

Scientific and technological progress in the Renaissance gave Europeans immense confidence, and in the 15th and 16th centuries they set out to explore the world. They discovered places they had no idea existed.

The European economy during the Renaissance

The European economy in the Renaissance was prosperous. But it was also fragile, because it depended mostly on agriculture. With every bad harvest, food became scarce and prices rose, which inevitably led to an economic crisis.

Europe produced common food items such as meat, fish, cereal, vegetables and wine. It also produced wool and flax for clothing, and metals for utensils and weapons. Europe harvested timber, too, although the massive forest clearances of the Middle Ages had drastically reduced the supply.

2.6 *Sheep shearing. Sixteenth-century miniature.*

Europeans imported gold, silver, precious stones, silk and spices. These luxury goods were brought to Europe from Africa and Asia by Arab and Italian traders.

2.7 EUROPEAN KINGDOMS IN THE 16TH CENTURY

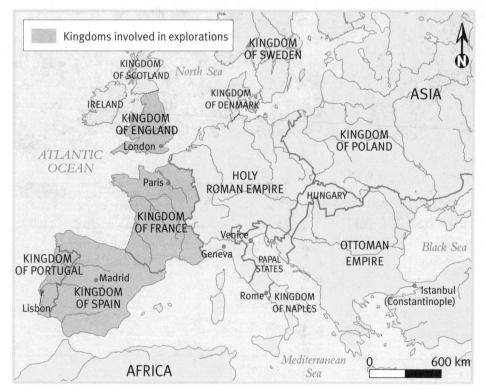

In the 15th and 16th centuries, Europe was made up of numerous independent countries, some of which were at war with their closest neighbours.

According to this map, what seems to be the most common political system in 16th-century Europe? Who governed the country under this type of system?

The American continent, unknown to Europeans

In the 10th century, Vikings from Scandinavia built small settlements on the coast of Newfoundland. Later, Basque fishermen occasionally landed on North American shores. Yet 15th-century Europeans were unaware of the existence of the vast American continent. Meanwhile, the indigenous peoples who lived throughout America were equally unaware of Europe.

2.8 PARTS OF THE WORLD KNOWN TO 15TH-CENTURY EUROPEANS

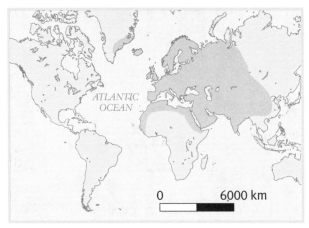

Which continents did Europeans know about in the 15th century (green on the map)? Which were only partly known? Which were completely unknown?

2.9 PEOPLES OF THE AMERICAN CONTINENT IN THE 15TH CENTURY

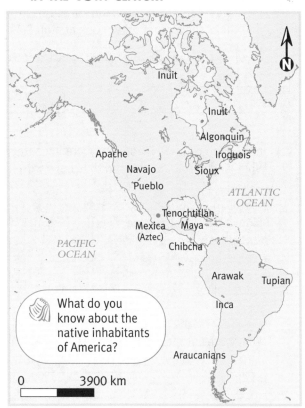

What do you know about the native inhabitants of America?

The inhabitants of the American continent were fishers, hunters and gatherers, or farmers. They traded with one another and, like other nations, formed political and military alliances. This map shows only a few of the hundreds of nations that peopled America in the 15th century. It is estimated that about 2,000 languages were spoken.

2.10 EUROPEAN EXPANSION DURING THE RENAISSANCE

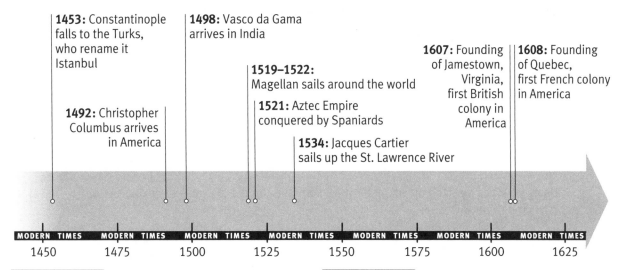

1453: Constantinople falls to the Turks, who rename it Istanbul

1492: Christopher Columbus arrives in America

1498: Vasco da Gama arrives in India

1519–1522: Magellan sails around the world

1521: Aztec Empire conquered by Spaniards

1534: Jacques Cartier sails up the St. Lawrence River

1607: Founding of Jamestown, Virginia, first British colony in America

1608: Founding of Quebec, first French colony in America

MODERN TIMES   MODERN TIMES   MODERN TIMES   MODERN TIMES   MODERN TIMES   MODERN TIMES   MODERN TIMES
1450   1475   1500   1525   1550   1575   1600   1625

Scandinavia: northern region of Europe consisting of Denmark, Sweden and Norway.

Basque: from the Basque country, a region straddling the border between Spain and France.

indigenous peoples: native people, or the people who first inhabit a region.

Let's Get to Work!

1 There were four main European kingdoms involved in exploration. What did they have in common, in terms of their geography? Look at map 2.7 on page 38 to help you find the answer.

All in Europe on the Atlatic coast. Western part of Europe.

2 In the 15th century, Europeans were in contact with Asians and Africans.
What kind of relationship did they have with them? Check the right answer.

○ political
○ cultural
☑ economic
○ religious

3 What were Europeans seeking in Asia and Africa?

They wanted gold, silver and spices (luxury goods)

4 a) Look at maps 2.7, 2.8 and 2.9 and use their scales to calculate the following distances:

1. From Istanbul to Lisbon (map 2.7, page 38): _____

2. From Central America to Spain (map 2.8, page 39): _____

3. From the northern tip of North America to the southern tip of South America (map 2.9, page 39):
_____

b) Using your answers to part a), compare the size of Europe with

1. the size of North and South America: _____
_____

2. the distance from Europe to America: _Very far in terms of distance._
_____
_____

c) Using your answers to part a) and part b), comment on the distance the explorers had to travel to cross the Atlantic Ocean.

They had to go on very long journeys.
_____
_____

Project

Contact with Europeans was traumatic for the indigenous peoples of America. Although nowadays they must follow the laws and political systems of the states in which they live, indigenous peoples still consider themselves distinct societies. Because of their differences, they claim various specific rights.

Task: In this Inquiry, we ask you to reflect on claims currently made by indigenous peoples of the American continent and on the links between these claims and indigenous ancestral rights.

Final product required: A news broadcast or a sketch.

Several steps are necessary to complete the project. Use the Project Planning Guide that your teacher will give you.

1 In teams, choose one indigenous group in North or South America. Your teacher can give you a list of them to choose from. Create a workplan and a timetable, then divide up the tasks.

2 Collect as much information as possible on your chosen indigenous group using the following questions:
- How was their society organized before contact with Europeans?
- How did the first meeting with Europeans go?
- How is their society organized today (economy, politics, language, religion, education, etc.)?
- What are their current claims?
- What are their difficulties in having their claims recognized? Why are they having these difficulties?

3 Collect all this information in a research file.

4 In your team, discuss the connections between your chosen group's claims today and the type of colonization they experienced in the past.

5 Prepare your news broadcast or sketch. Find an original way to present the claims that your chosen group is making in the name of their ancestral rights.

Why Did Europeans Set Out to Explore the World?

As you know, Europeans had been trading with Asia and Africa since the Middle Ages. During the Renaissance, the old trade routes to Asia became less accessible. Many European countries embarked on a feverish race across unknown waters to find new trade routes. Their explorations were driven by political and religious motives as well as commercial ones. New navigation techniques made the voyages possible.

Economic motives

Gold was the main currency used for world trade during the Renaissance. A large increase in population led to more trade, which in turn led to a greater demand for gold. Europeans mined gold in Europe and Africa, but the goldfields in both places were running out. Marco Polo reported that China and Japan were brimming with gold and other precious resources.

Most Asian merchandise destined for Europe was purchased from Arab traders by Italian merchants. They mostly brought it to Europe via Constantinople, an important crossroads linking Europe and Asia (you can find it on map 2.7). In 1453, Muslim Turks captured Constantinople, renamed it Istanbul and imposed harsh **duties** on trade. Now that there were Turkish as well as Italian and Arab **middlemen**, European countries decided to bypass them all by going to fetch the coveted goods themselves. They raced against each other to find new maritime routes to India and China. This was the goal which set in motion the "Age of Discovery" that began in the late 15th century.

Did you know...

马可波罗（马可波罗大约在1254年至1324年间）是意大利威尼斯们的商人，17岁时，他的父亲和叔叔把他带到中国，为中国皇帝工作了约20年，当他回到意大利时，马可波罗向他的朋友讲述了他的旅行故事，他在"马可·波罗之书"中写到了这本书，书中包含了马可波罗对中国、日本和印度的描述。他们同时代人很难相信他对这种神秘想象的富饶描述，但200年后，像...这样的探险家受到了"马可波罗"的启发。

Marco Polo's travels in Asia, 1271–95.

MARCO POLO (circa 1254 to 1324)

Marco Polo's family were merchants in Venice, Italy. When he was only 17 years old, his father and uncle took him with them to China.

For about 20 years he worked for the Chinese Emperor, who sent him on various missions.

When he came back to Italy, Marco Polo recounted tales of his voyages to his friend Rustichello de Pisa, who wrote about them in *The Book of Ser Marco Polo*. The book contains Marco Polo's descriptions of China, Japan and India.

His contemporaries found it hard to believe his descriptions of such fabulous riches. But 200 years later, explorers such as Christopher Columbus and Vasco da Gama were inspired by *The Book of Ser Marco Polo*.

---

duties: government taxes on imports or exports.

middleman: trader who buys from producers and sells to consumers.

✴ THE BOOK OF SER MARCO POLO (1298–1307)

The Book of Ser Marco Polo was written between 1298 and 1307. Europeans were dazzled by Marco Polo's glowing account of the riches of Asia. Here are a few excerpts:

> "The walls of the Palace are all covered with gold and silver ... I tell you, no day in the year passes that there do not enter the city a thousand cart-loads of silk alone, from which are made quantities of cloth of silk and gold, and of other goods. And this is not to be wondered at; for in all the countries round about there is no flax, so that everything has to be made of silk ... They have also ginger and cinnamon in great plenty, besides other spices."

The Book of Ser Marco Polo, the Venetian, Concerning the Kingdoms and Marvels of the East. Translated by Henry Yule. London: J. Murray, 1871.

The pepper harvest. Miniature from The Book of Ser Marco Polo.

Spices were highly prized by Europeans. Pepper, cloves, cinnamon and nutmeg brought a touch of the exotic to the tables of the rich. Spices were also used by pharmacists.

 Name some of the things you eat that come from outside Quebec. Where do they come from? How do they get here?

Political motives

Europeans also had political motives for exploring the world. European monarchs perpetually tried to increase their territory so they could gain access to more resources and control larger populations. Possibilities for growth were limited in Europe, however, where every attempt to expand led to armed conflict with one's neighbour. Conquering distant lands became an attractive alternative for many monarchs.

Religious motives

Europeans went exploring for religious reasons too. Asians and Africans were not Christians, and the Church wanted to bring Christianity to all pagans.

The Counter-Reformation, which began in the 16th century as a reaction against Protestantism, renewed religious faith and the desire to evangelize, or attempt to convince pagans to convert peacefully to Christianity. This situation inspired the founding of the religious order known as the Society of Jesus, or the Jesuits. Its mission was to bring the Catholic faith to all pagan peoples.

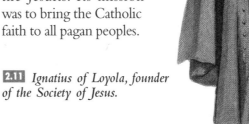

2.11 *Ignatius of Loyola, founder of the Society of Jesus.*

---

monarch: king or queen.

pagan: a person who practises a religion other than Christianity, Judaism or Islam.

Let's Get to Work!

1 a) Locate the following events on the timeline below.

1455   1. The invention of the printing press   印刷机的发明.

1298-1307   2. The publication of *The Book of Ser Marco Polo*   马可·波罗的书出版

1492   3. Christopher Columbus's arrival in America   克里斯托弗·哥伦布.

Look at the timelines on pages 6 and 39 to help you.

Write the years under the timeline at 100-year intervals (1200, 1300, etc.).

1298-1307 The publication of the Book of ser Marco Polo   *1455 The invention of the printing press.*   *1492 Christopher Columbus's arrival in America*

1300   1400   1500   1600   1700   1800   1900   2000

b) Do you think there are any cause-and-effect connections among these three events? Explain your answer.

the invention of the printing press distributed the book of ser marco polo, which inspired explorers to search for a passage to find the riches described by Marco Polo.

2 Reread the passages of *The Book of Ser Marco Polo* on page 43 and list the products that were most sought after by Europeans in the 15th century.

Gold and silver, silk and spices

3 Marco Polo recounted his voyages to a friend, Rustichello de Pisa, who wrote them down in *The Book of Ser Marco Polo*. Read this passage from the prologue to the book and then answer the questions.

> "Take this Book and cause it to be read to you. For ye shall find therein all kinds of wonderful things ... of India, and of many another country of which our Book doth speak, particularly and in regular succession, according to the description of Messer Marco Polo, a wise and noble citizen of Venice, as he saw them with his own eyes. Some things indeed there be therein which he beheld not; but these he heard from men of credit and veracity ... all who shall read it or hear it read may put full faith in the truth of all its contents."
>
> *The Book of Ser Marco Polo, the Venetian, Concerning the Kingdoms and Marvels of the East.*
> Translated by Henry Yule. London: J. Murray, 1871.

a) Who saw the marvels described in the book, according to this passage?

Marco Polo

b) According to this passage, why should the reader believe the things that Marco Polo did not see with his own eyes?

because Marco Polo heard them from men of credit and veracity.

My History Log

c) Do you think *The Book of Ser Marco Polo* is a credible source? Give reasons for your answer.

personal opinion

d) If someone told you she had discovered gold, would you believe her? Why?

proof, you need to know who you are talking about

4 Use this table to write down the three main motives for European explorations, and explain each motive.

5 What was the main motive for the voyages of discovery?

To find new trade routes to Asia

6 Which two European motives for exploration are represented by symbols in this picture? Check the right answers.

◯ The search for commodities

✓ The desire to evangelize the pagans

✓ The need to expand a kingdom's territory

◯ The taste for adventure

◯ The desire for scientific knowledge

Cross planted by Jacques Cartier in Gaspé in 1534.

Advances in astronomy

To set out across unknown waters, explorers needed more than the desire to do it. They needed knowledge and technology.

In the Middle Ages, people generally believed that the world was flat, as the Church taught. Sailors were afraid to go too far across the sea in case they fell off the edge of the world. But when scholars rediscovered the writings of classical antiquity in the 15th century, they became convinced that the world was round. The timeline below shows advances in astronomy that were made in the 16th and 17th centuries.

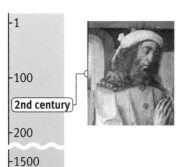

CLAUDIUS PTOLEMEUS, KNOWN AS PTOLEMY (circa 90 AD to circa 168 AD)

The Greek astronomer Ptolemy believed that the Earth was spherical, that it was located at the centre of the universe, and that the heavenly bodies revolved around it. This theory was known as geocentrism (the prefix *geo-* means earth).

2.12 *Geocentrism.*

✳ NICOLAUS COPERNICUS (1473 to 1543)

In his book *On the Revolutions of the Celestial Spheres*, Copernicus disputed Ptolemy's theory that the Earth was at the centre of the universe. He thought instead that all the planets, including the Earth, orbited around the Sun. This theory was known as heliocentrism (the prefix *helio-* means sun). After Copernicus died the Church denounced his theory.

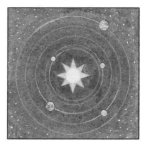

2.13 *Heliocentrism.*

✳ GALILEO GALILEI (1564 to 1642)

Galileo built several telescopes (one of them magnified objects 20 times) for observing the heavenly bodies. With his telescopes he discovered four moons of Jupiter, the rings of Saturn and sunspots. His observations led him to conclude that the Earth rotated on its own axis as well as orbiting around the Sun, thus confirming Copernicus's hypothesis. He had to retract his theory before a Church tribunal to avoid the death penalty, even though he was sure he was right.

✳ JOHANNES KEPLER (1571 to 1630)

Kepler was a friend of Galileo's who worked out three mathematical laws to explain the movements of the heavenly bodies. He deduced that their orbit was not circular but elliptical (oval-shaped). However, he was unable to clearly explain why.

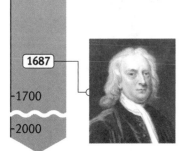

✳ ISAAC NEWTON (1642 to 1727)

Newton formulated a mathematical hypothesis called the Law of Universal Gravitation. This law says that heavenly bodies, such as the Sun and the planets, are attracted to one another in proportion to their mass and the distance between them. His law explained the elliptical orbit of the planets, the movements of the Moon, the phenomenon of tides and the slightly squashed shape of the Earth.

Timeline:
-1
-100
[2nd century]
-200
-1500
1543
-1600
1609
1618
1687
-1700
-2000

Advances in navigation

To set out across the Atlantic Ocean, the explorers needed ships that were easy to handle, that were built for long voyages and that they could steer in high seas. The following inventions made important contributions to the voyages of European maritime explorers of the 15th and 16th centuries.

The caravel

In the 15th century, the Portuguese developed a new ship called a caravel. It was a small ship with high sides. Its wide bottom made it stable on sea crossings. It had a triangular sail, called a lateen, which meant it could make use of winds coming from the side and even from the front. The Arabs introduced the lateen sail to Europe from India. Another innovation was the sternpost rudder. It was attached to a post at the back (stern) of the ship and made it easier to steer.

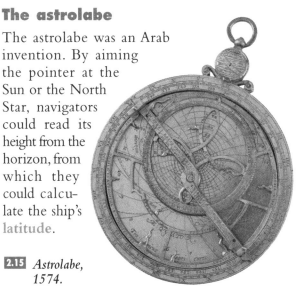

2.14 *The* Santa Maria *was one of the three caravels used in Christopher Columbus's expedition. Engraving from the 16th century.*

lateen sail

sternpost rudder

The astrolabe

The astrolabe was an Arab invention. By aiming the pointer at the Sun or the North Star, navigators could read its height from the horizon, from which they could calculate the ship's latitude.

2.15 *Astrolabe, 1574.*

The compass

The compass was introduced into Europe from China in the 12th century and improved by the Portuguese in the 15th century. It consists of a small box filled with water or oil with a magnetic needle floating on top, which points to the magnetic north. The advantage of a compass is that it can be read in any weather and at night as well as in daytime.

© Musée national de la Marine/P. Dantec

2.16 *Steering compass, Ferreira Manoel, 1744, Lisbon.*

The portolan

Portolans were navigation charts, often bound like a book, illustrating shorelines, islands and the location of ports. The charts were made by Italians, Portuguese and Spaniards. They were used alongside the astrolabe and the compass to determine a ship's position and to set it on the right course.

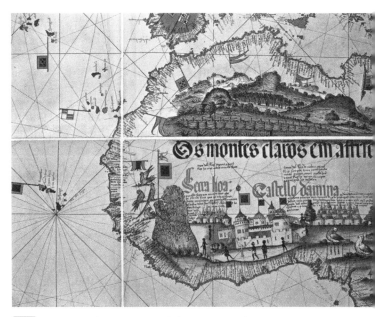

2.17 *Portolan showing part of the coast of Africa, 1502.*

 Can you name any improvements in navigation since the caravel?

latitude: distance from the equator.

Let's Get to Work!

1 Explorers did not get very far across the Atlantic Ocean until the 15th century. Why not? Give at least two reasons.

They thought they were going to fall the edge of the earth, they did not have any ships or navigation tools to said across the ocean.

2 Once they were sure that the Earth was round, where did the explorers think they would land once they had crossed the Atlantic Ocean? Why? Look at map 2.8 on page 39 to help you find the answer.

Asia, because they did not know America existed.

3 Name the scientist responsible for each of the theories below.

Ptolemy • Copernicus • Galileo • Kepler • Newton

a) The orbit of heavenly bodies is not circular. ____ *Kepler* ____

b) The Earth is round and is situated at the centre of the universe. ____ *ptolemy* ____

c) Heavenly bodies are attracted to one another because of gravity. ____ *Newton* ____

d) Saturn has rings and Jupiter has at least four moons. ____ *Galileo* ____

e) The Earth is round and orbits around the Sun. ____ *Copernicus* ____

4 For each of these astronomers, indicate whether they verified their hypotheses using mathematical laws or direct observation. Rèread page 46 to help you answer.

	MATHEMATICAL LAW	DIRECT OBSERVATION
a) Galileo	○	☑
b) Kepler	☑	○
c) Newton	☑	○

5 a) Which of the following inventions were European and which were non-European?

	EUROPEAN INVENTION	NON-EUROPEAN INVENTION
1. Compass	○	☑
2. Astrolabe	○	☑
3. Caravel	☑	○
4. Lateen sail	○	☑

b) What social group do you think introduced these inventions into Europe? How did they find out about them?

merchants or traders. They found out about them because they frequently traded with Asia

6 a) Imagine you are a Spanish explorer of the Renaissance who wants to set out across the Atlantic Ocean. You want the king to finance your journey. Write a proposal describing your goals, the technology you will use, the resources that you need and why you are confident the enterprise will succeed.

My voyage of discovery

Goals of the journey:

- Wanted to search for gold (gold)
- Wanted to expand territories (glory)
- To spread the teachings of christianity to all pagans (god)

Technology:
– for sailing: _the lateen sail. the caravel. the sternpost rudder_
– for navigating: _compass. portolan (map) astrolabe_

Resources needed:
water. Cook. vitamin C. crew (sailors, captain). money to finance these voyages

Reasons for confidence in the success of the enterprise:

b) Your king asks you to secure the support of at least two social groups. Which groups would you approach? Why?

1. First group: _Merchants_
   I would approach this group because _they made profits off selling their resources._

2. Second group: _Religious communities such as the Jesuits._
   I would approach this group because _to convert all pagans._

How Did Europeans Come to Dominate the World?

In their search for new maritime routes to Asia, the Europeans discovered lands they didn't know existed. They took control over the people who lived in those lands.

Voyages of exploration

The funds needed for organizing the major voyages of exploration in the 15th and 16th centuries were provided by European monarchs, with the support of the nobility and the merchant middle classes.

The explorers who headed for Asia via the western route across the Atlantic Ocean gradually realized their mistake: what they thought was the coast of Asia was in fact a new continent. Many explorers continued to search for a westward route by sailing around this vast continent. Others decided to look for riches by crossing it overland.

Research mandate

Do some research about conditions on board ship in the 15th and 16th centuries.

2.13 THE GREAT DISCOVERIES

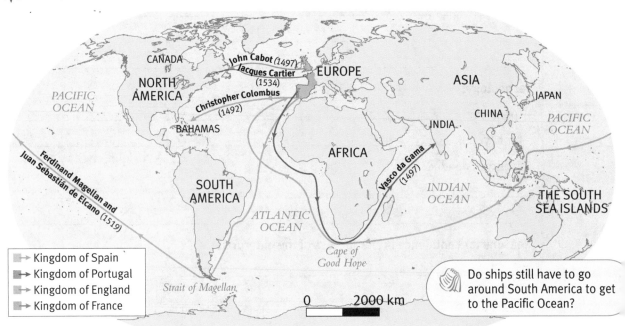

Kingdom of Spain
Kingdom of Portugal
Kingdom of England
Kingdom of France

Do ships still have to go around South America to get to the Pacific Ocean?

- In 1492, Christopher Columbus, an Italian explorer in the service of Spain, sailed to the islands of the Bahamas, in the Caribbean, and took possession of them in the name of the king and queen of Spain. Believing he had reached India, he named the islands "The West Indies" and called their inhabitants "Indians."
- In 1497, the Portuguese explorer Vasco da Gama attempted to reach Asia, not by sailing westward like Columbus but southeast around the Cape of Good Hope at the southern tip of Africa. His quest was successful and he landed in Calicut, India.
- In 1497, John Cabot, an Italian explorer in the service of England, sought a passage to Asia via the northwest. He sailed up the coast of Newfoundland and Labrador, thus becoming the first European to officially discover Canada.
- Ferdinand Magellan and Juan Sebastián de Elcano left Spain in 1519 and circumnavigated the globe westward, sailing around South America. They were the first to sail into a new ocean which they named the Pacific Ocean. Magellan was killed on the journey and de Elcano sailed home to Spain around the southern tip of Africa.
- In 1534, Jacques Cartier explored the mouth of the St. Lawrence River on behalf of the king of France. The next year he sailed upriver as far as the site of the future city of Montreal.

Contact with indigenous peoples

Christopher Columbus told Europeans about a new continent, which they would later call America. However, it had been inhabited for thousands of years. Although Europeans and indigenous people introduced each other to new goods, there was mutual misunderstanding from the very first contact.

Here is how Christopher Columbus described the inhabitants of America:

> "They all go as naked as when their mothers bore them, even the women ... Weapons they have none, nor are acquainted with them, for I showed them swords, which they grasped by the blades and cut themselves through ignorance ... I am of the opinion that they would very readily become Christians, as they appear to have no religion."
>
> Christopher Columbus's Ship's Logbook, 1492.
> From *First Voyage to America: From the Log of the "Santa Maria."* Mineola, NY: Dover Pubns, 1992.

Europeans introduced the indigenous peoples to many new items, while indigenous peoples taught the explorers about new plant species. They took these plants back and introduced them into Europe.

Europeans ⇩ Indigenous peoples	Indigenous peoples ⇩ Europeans
• barley, rye, wheat • vines • sheep • cows • horses • metal objects (knives, fish hooks, etc.) • firearms	• pineapple • chocolate • tomatoes • beans • corn • potatoes • tobacco

You must have heard people speak of the "New World" and the "Old World." Which continents does each term refer to? Why do we use these names?

2.19 *Christopher Columbus landing in America in 1492. Engraving by Theodore de Bry, 16th century.*

What can you tell about the attitude of the Spaniards from this engraving? The attitude of indigenous people? Can you explain why it only took about 100 Europeans to conquer America?

Let's Get to Work!

1 a) What was Christopher Columbus looking for when he crossed the Atlantic Ocean westward?

_____

b) Where did he end up?

_____

2 What do you think were some of the problems that 15th-century explorers faced?

_____

_____

3 Voyages of discovery were very expensive. Why do you think this was? Give at least two reasons.

_____

_____

_____

4 a) In the table below, fill in the details about the great discoveries of the 15th and 16th centuries. Name the explorer, the country he came from and the discovery he made. Look at map 2.18 on page 50 to help you find the answers.

Date	Explorer	Country	Exploration
1492	Christopher Colombus	Spain	Christopher Columbus discovered a land that was unknown to Europeans
1497	Vasco da Gama		
1519			
1534			

b) Name one consequence of each of these explorations.

1492: The Europeans explored the continent discovered by Christopher Columbus.

1497: _____

1519: _____

1534: _____

5) Christopher Columbus made two geographical mistakes. What do you think were the consequences of each of his mistakes?

a) Mistake: The Earth is four times larger than Columbus thought.
Consequence for the length of his voyage:

_____

b) Mistake: Columbus didn't know that America existed.
Consequence for how he named the inhabitants of the continent:

_____

6) Christopher Columbus owned a copy of *The Book of Ser Marco Polo*. What do you think he hoped to find in Asia?

_____

7) Which were the first two European kingdoms to undertake major explorations? Look at map 2.18 on page 50 to help you find the answer.

_____

8) The following people helped convince Europeans that the Earth was round.
Link each person to the technique he used.

a) Copernicus   1. Proof

b) Galileo   2. Observations using instruments

c) Magellan   3. Hypothesis

9) We use the term "Pre-Columbian" for America before 1492. Why, do you think?

_____

_____

10) "The Age of Discovery" refers to the 15th and 16th centuries when Europeans were exploring the world. Why is this term used? Give two reasons.

_____

_____

_____

11) Study figure 2.19 on page 51. This engraving was done by a European artist in Christopher Columbus's lifetime. Describe how this artist perceived the indigenous people.

_____

_____

_____

Europeans colonize the world

Convinced of the superiority of their civilization, Europeans took possession of the lands they found. They began to exploit the resources and dominate the populations of these lands. This is called colonization.

A sense of superiority

In the Renaissance, Europeans believed their civilization was better than any other. They believed their religion, science, technology, political systems, etc. were superior. Their military victories over indigenous peoples only reinforced this conviction. They began to try to impose their culture on the indigenous people.

From first contact between indigenous people and Europeans, it was clear that the two had completely different perceptions of the world, as the table below shows.

These different worldviews led to misunderstandings. In North America, for example, when indigenous people traded goods with Europeans, they assumed the Europeans were their allies.

They were astonished to discover that the same Europeans were also trading with their enemies.

Exploiting the natural resources of the colonies

The kingdoms of Europe quickly took possession of the newly discovered lands and colonized them, exploiting them for profit. Many kingdoms built entire colonial empires this way.

There were two types of colony:
– The colony of exploitation, occupied only by soldiers and merchants who sent commodities from the colony back to the mother country;
– The colony of settlement, with permanent settlers of every trade and profession, men and women who had come over from Europe.

Research mandate

During the Renaissance, some people called the indigenous people "savages." Research the various definitions of this word, and use them to explain how certain Europeans perceived indigenous peoples.

	European view	Indigenous view
The human being's place in nature	• Humans must dominate nature.	• Humans must live in harmony with nature.
The trading of goods	• Trading is mostly a commercial activity. Money is exchanged.	• Trade has economic, religious, political, military and social significance. Goods are exchanged using barter.
Laws	• Laws are written down.	• Laws are orally transmitted.
Political power	• Europeans are organized into large states. • The king commands, his subjects obey.	• North American indigenous people are organized into small tribes. • The chief of a tribe has the power to persuade, but not to command.
Production	• Surpluses are produced so that they can be sold for profit.	• People produce only what they need.
Land	• Property is privately owned and results in social inequality. Society accepts that poverty and wealth may coexist. • Land belongs to the country that finds it.	• Private property doesn't exist. Goods are shared among the members of the community. • The land belongs to no one.

---

empire: group of colonies ruled by a single authority.
colony: territory ruled by another country.

mother country: the country of origin of settlers or colonists.
barter: trade without the use of money.

Many North American colonies were set up as trading posts for the fur trade with the indigenous peoples. One such colony was Quebec, founded in 1608. Other colonies, such as Virginia, focused instead on settlement.

In both cases, the natural resources of the colonies were shipped back home to the mother country for processing. The economy of the colony itself was thus unable to grow.

2.20 *The fur trade in New France.*
What do you think the people in this painting are doing?

2.21 COLONIAL EMPIRES OF THE 17TH CENTURY

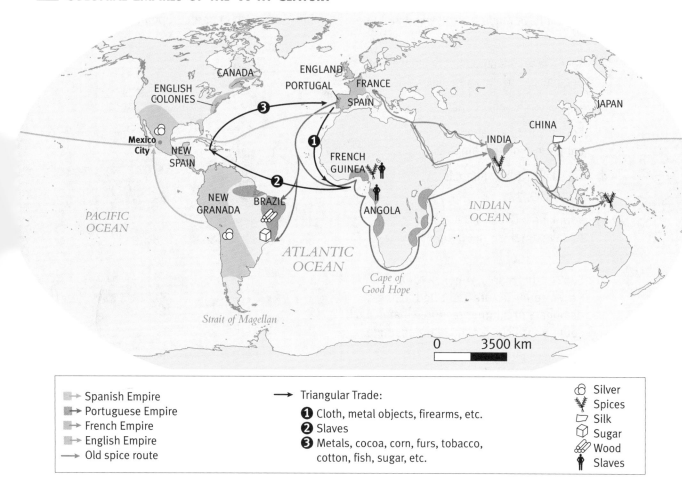

With the colonization of America, Africa and part of Asia, two major maritime trade routes were added to overseas trade.

– The maritime route linking Europe with Asia via southern Africa (in blue on the map);

– The triangular maritime trade route linking Europe, Africa and America (in black on the map);

The new routes made a new "world economy" possible, as trading began to take place on a worldwide scale. Europeans dominated this trade.

Let's Get to Work!

1 Use the table on page 54 to answer the following questions.

a) What two reasons did the Europeans give to justify their domination of the indigenous peoples?

They had weapons and the were wealthier

Europeans with pose with of the lands they found.

b) Give two reasons why the indigenous people had difficulty defending themselves against the Europeans.

they did not have any firearms. they did not have any knowledge.
in terms of combat.

2 Who might have made the following statements, an indigenous chief or a European captain?

	INDIGENOUS CHIEF	EUROPEAN CAPTAIN
a) Take these furs and bead necklaces and become our friends and allies.	✓	○
b) This land belongs to me.	○	✓
c) I order you to kill anyone who comes into our encampment.	○	✓
d) Let's kill as many animals as we can.	○	✓
e) Your king must be very poor to have to take other peoples' land.	✓	○

3 a) Look at this map of America today. Seven countries are identified. Using a dictionary or another resource, name each country's official language or languages.

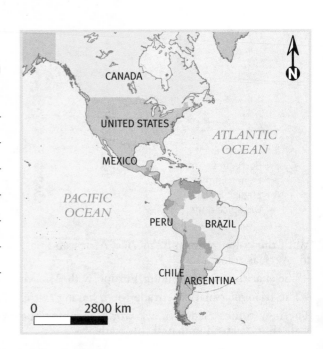

1. Canada: _English. French._

2. United States: _English._

3. Mexico: _Spanish_

4. Brazil: _Portuguese_

5. Peru: _spanish_

6. Chile: _spanish_

7. Argentina: _spanish._

b) Are the languages you wrote down in part a) indigenous or European?
Why is this?

European. because the Europeans imposed their languages on the
inhabitants of america when they colonized it.

4 Here is an excerpt from an account of a voyage to New France in the 17th century. Read it and answer the questions.

"Through them you will be able to establish a commerce yielding almost incredible profits, because with baubles such as bells, brass rings, trumpets ... you will be able to obtain a variety of precious merchandise."

Paul Boyer, *Véritable relation de tout ce qui s'est fait et passé au voyage que Monsieur de Brétigny fit à l'Amérique Occidentale*, 1654. From *The Myth of the Savage and the Beginnings of French Colonialism in the Americas* by O.P. Dickason. University of Alberta Press, 1984.

a) What does the word "bauble" mean? Look it up in the dictionary if you don't know.

_____

b) Why do you think the indigenous people accepted baubles in trade exchanges with Europeans? Look at the table on page 54 to help you find the answer.

_____

_____

_____

_____

5 Compared to the old trade routes, were the new world economy trade routes

◯ longer?

◯ shorter?

◯ the same length?

6 Among the following peoples, who benefited most from the new trade routes? Who lost out? Highlight in blue the people who won out and in yellow the people who lost out.

a) the Arabs   c) the French   e) the Spaniards

b) the Portuguese   d) the Italians   f) the English

7 a) Look at map 2.21 on page 55. In the triangular trade, which products came from

1. America? _____

_____

2. Europe? _____

3. Africa? _____

b) Which of these continents dominated trade? _____

The effects of colonization on the conquered peoples

The colonizers took possession of North and South America mostly by force. They disturbed the political alliances that indigenous peoples had made with one another, causing new conflicts to flare up. For indigenous people, colonization had disastrous consequences that are still being felt today.

Contact with Europeans was catastrophic for the indigenous peoples. It led to a dramatic decline in population.

The high death rate was mostly due to epidemics and, to a lesser extent, massacres and forced labour.

Changes in the indigenous population

- Circa 1492: About 80 million
- Circa 1550: About 10 million

 Do you know what proportion of today's population of North and South America is indigenous?

Epidemics

Europeans brought infectious diseases with them without realizing it, and indigenous people's immune systems had no resistance to these diseases. Measles, smallpox, flu and the plague all decimated the indigenous peoples of the American continent.

Massacres

In Central and South America, the **conquistadors** destroyed the Mexica (or Aztec) and Inca civilizations. Outraged by the violence, a Spanish priest, Bartolomé de Las Casas, reported the atrocities committed by the Spanish colonizers to the King of Spain, Charles V. Las Casas demanded that the king put an end to the massacres. They continued anyway.

✳ "They [the Spaniards] forced their way into native settlements, slaughtering everyone they found there, including small children, old men, pregnant women, and even women who had just given birth. They hacked them to pieces, slicing open their bellies with their swords as though they were so many sheep herded into a pen. They even laid wagers on whether they could manage to slice a man in two at a stroke, or cut an individual's head from his body, or disembowel him with a single blow of their axes."

Bartolomé de Las Casas, *A Short Account of the Destruction of the Indies, 1542.* Translation and Notes © Nigel Griffin, 1992. Introduction © Anthony Pagden, 1992.

Mexica (Aztec) sculpture.

✳ TENOCHTITLAN

In 1325, the Mexica (Aztecs) built their capital city of Tenochtitlan in a swampy part of Lake Texcoco, the site of Mexico City today. In the 14th and 15th centuries, they conquered several other peoples and founded an empire that gradually extended over Mexico and northern Guatemala. They created a remarkable civilization which lasted for two centuries.

This civilization came to an abrupt end when the conquistador Hernán Cortés conquered Mexico. Although they put up a struggle, the Mexica were unable to hold back the Spaniards, who fought with guns and had made alliances with the enemies of the Mexica. In 1521, Cortés captured the city, which had a population of 500,000 at the time, and destroyed it.

Research mandate

What was the city of Tenochtitlan like? How did the Spaniards destroy it? Do some research to find out.

conquistador: 16th-century Spanish conqueror.

2.22 *Black slaves working for the conquistadors in the gold mines of America.*

Forced labour

In some colonies, the European colonizers forced the indigenous people into slave labour in gold and silver mines.

In 1537, Pope Paul III forbade the enslavement of indigenous people. This ban was mostly ignored, but as there were fewer and fewer indigenous people available, Europeans of the mid-16th century turned to another source of labour: black slaves from Africa. This was the beginning of the African slave trade and the triangular trade (see map 2.21, page 55).

From the 16th to the 19th century, between 12 and 20 million African slaves were brought to America to labour in mines and in plantations growing cocoa, coffee, tobacco, cotton, etc.

Economic dependence

The mother country imported raw materials from its colonies, processed them, and sold them back to

colonists as manufactured goods. The colony thus became economically dependent on the mother country. In North America, for example, indigenous nomadic peoples began hunting animals sought by Europeans for the fur trade. The nomadic peoples' age-old trade with sedentary indigenous groups stopped, and instead they bought food and other goods from the Europeans. They became accustomed to European weapons, tools, utensils etc., and gradually came to depend on them.

Indigenous nomads were encouraged to stay in one place. Europeans imposed their own laws on indigenous peoples and compelled them to live on reserves if they wanted to keep certain rights. People on reserves would henceforth depend on the newcomers for their livelihood.

 Are there any First Nations reserves in your region? Do you know when they were established?

---

raw materials: natural resources that are processed into manufactured goods.

sedentary: living in one place; not nomadic.
First Nations: term used in Canada for some indigenous groups.

Cultural loss

Indigenous people did not live the way Europeans did. They practised **polygamy**, wore few clothes, ate on the ground and at irregular times, etc. Europeans thought that these customs were strange, and that indigenous people behaved like this because they did not believe in God. Europeans therefore began to evangelize them. European religious beliefs were very different from those of the indigenous people, however, as shown in the table below.

Many indigenous people converted to Christianity and became sedentary. North American indigenous people were less likely than others to convert. **Missionaries** sometimes offered to give them guns if they agreed to be baptized. Their conversion led to profound changes in their cultures. Their languages, for example, were gradually replaced by those of the conquerors.

2.23 *Religious sisters teaching indigenous children in Quebec City in 1640.*

DIFFERENCES BETWEEN CHRISTIANITY AND INDIGENOUS RELIGIONS	
Christianity	**Indigenous religions**
• Christianity is a monotheistic religion (only recognizes one God).	• Indigenous religions are animist: every aspect of nature is a manifestation of the divine.
• Religious feasts celebrate various events in the life of Jesus.	• Religious ritual includes sacrifices, offerings, dances and prayers.
• The priest or minister uses the Bible to guide the spiritual life of the faithful.	• The shaman interprets dreams and treats the sick.

2.24 *Indigenous shaman.*

Did you know... Did you know... Did you know... Did you know... Did you know... Did you know...

INDIGENOUS PEOPLES AND POLYGAMY

In the 16th century, indigenous people were polygamous. A man could have several wives.

The Christians were scandalized by this practice, which may have existed because there were more indigenous women than men.

In addition, polygamy fit the needs of people who were constantly in survival mode. A woman would never be without support: if her husband died, another man could take her into his household as his second or third wife.

By outlawing polygamy, European missionaries forced indigenous people to change their social structures.

Did you know... Did you know... Did you know... Did you know... Did you know...

---

polygamy: the custom of having more than one wife at the same time.

missionary: someone who is sent out to convert people to his or her religion.

Let's Get to Work!

1 By what percentage did the indigenous population drop between 1492 and 1550? Look at the small table on page 58. Show your calculations.

70 million divided by 80 million 80-10 x x100 = 87.5%.

2 a) Among the following groups of Europeans, which was the most likely to defend indigenous peoples? Check the right answer.

○ Merchants

○ Colonizers

☑ Religious communities

○ Scholars

○ Monarchs

b) Why do you think this group defended indigenous peoples?

Because they wanted to convert them. they believed that they had souls.

3 What was the main cause of death among indigenous people in the colonial era?

~~Diseases~~ _Diseases ._

4 Why do you think the title of Bartolomé de Las Casas' book, written in 1542, mentions the Indies but not the Americas?

Because when christopher columbus arrived to America he thought he had reached India.

5 The following aspects of European culture were integrated into indigenous cultures. Beside each aspect of European culture, name an indigenous one that had to be abandoned.

Aspect of European culture	Aspect of indigenous culture
Private property	Sharing among community members
Trade based on profit	_Barter or the political, social and military signilioance of trade_
European languages	_indigenous languages._
Christianity	_animist religion._

6 a) In the passages below, Europeans present their views on indigenous peoples. Read the passages and highlight the words that refer to the positive and negative characteristics the Europeans attributed to indigenous people.

1.

"Being by nature slaves, barbarians, uncultured and inhumane, they refuse to accept the domination of those who are more prudent, powerful and perfect than they – domination that would bring them the greatest benefits, being, moreover, a just thing ... Wars of this nature can be undertaken by very civilized Nations against peoples who are uncivilized, who are indeed barbaric beyond imagining, as they are completely illiterate and know nothing of money."

Juan Ginés de Sepúlveda, *Defence of the Book on the Just Causes of War*, Valladolid Debates, 1550. Free translation.

2.

"The simplest people in the world – unassuming, long-suffering, unassertive, and submissive – they are without malice or guile, and are utterly faithful and obedient ... their delicate constitutions make them unable to withstand hard work ... Most of them go naked, save for a loincloth to cover their modesty ... They are innocent and pure in mind and have a lively intelligence, all of which makes them particularly receptive to learning and understanding the truths of our Catholic faith."

Bartolomé de Las Casas, *Short Account of the Destruction of the Indies, 1542*. Translation and Notes © Nigel Griffin, 1992. Introduction © Anthony Pagden, 1992.

3.

"[They are] naturally lazy and vicious, melancoholic, cowardly, and in general a lying, shiftless people. Their marriages are not a sacrament but a sacrilege."

Oviedo (royal historian of Spain), *Historia general*, 1353. From *The Struggle for Justice in the Conquest of America* by Lewis Hanke. Philadelphia: University of Pennsylvania Press, 1949.

b) Study these passages and name at least four cultural differences between the Europeans and indigenous peoples during the Renaissance.

- *different religions*
- *monogamy / polygamy.*
- *Indigenous   people wore fewer clothes.*
- *indigenous people were illiterate.*

c) Which of these three authors had contempt for indigenous people?

Juan Gines and Oviedo

d) Which one thought indigenous people should be slaves?

Juan Gines

e) What did Bartolomé Las Casas want?

He wanted to convert them

f) Explain the link between racism and slavery in your own words.

_____

_____

Synthesis Activities

1 The map below was drawn in 1595.

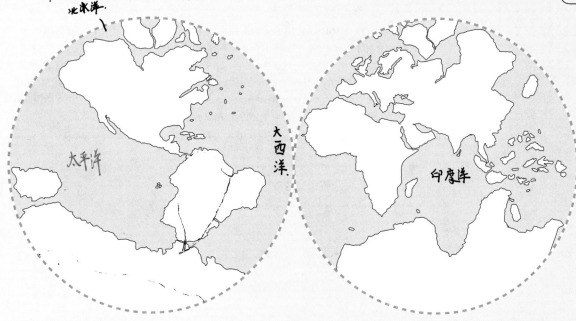

a) Write in the names of the continents and the main oceans.

b) Which continents are most accurately drawn?

_____

c) Which continents are less accurately drawn? Explain your answer.

_____

_____

2 Which European kingdoms explored

a) North America? _____

b) Central America? _____

c) South America? _____

d) the coast of Africa? _____

3 Describe the two maritime routes to India that were discovered during the Renaissance.
Which explorer discovered them?

a) First maritime route: _____

_____

Explorer who discovered it: _____

b) Second maritime route: _____

_____

Explorer who discovered it: _____

(4) Explain the phenomenon of the "Age of Discovery" in the 15th and 16th centuries by filling in the table below. Use the following words:

> The search for gold and precious metals • missionaries • evangelization (use twice) • the southeast route to Asia • caravel • roundness of the Earth • high death rate • merchants • the American continent • compass • the search for spices • colonization • monarchs • astrolabe • portolan • desire for more land • the coast of Africa • westward circumnavigation of the globe • slavery • advances in astronomy • economic dependence • sedentarization • sternpost rudder • lateen sail • explorers

THE AGE OF DISCOVERY

Motives

Economic motives:

_____

_____

_____

_____

Political motive:

_____

_____

Religious motive:

_____

_____

Methods

Scientific knowledge:

_____

_____

_____

Technological means:

_____

_____

_____

_____

_____

Main discoveries

_____

_____

_____

_____

_____

_____

_____

_____

_____

_____

People who conducted or financed expeditions

_____

_____

_____

_____

_____

_____

Consequences for the colonized peoples

_____

_____

_____

_____

_____

_____

Synthesis Activities

5 a) Explain how colonial empires worked by drawing a diagram that includes the following elements:

> mother country • colonial empire • trading post • settlers • colony

b) In which continent were the mother countries?_____

c) In which continents were the colonies?

_____

6 What was the main goal of the Europeans in creating the colonies? Check the correct answer.

○ Dominate the world and demonstrate that they were superior

○ Evangelize the indigenous people

○ Profit from controlling world trade

○ Put their scientific knowledge to the test

7 You have learned that overseas trade began to develop during the Middle Ages. Fill out the table below to show the links between medieval overseas trade and 16th-century colonial trade.

In the Middle Ages	In the 16th century
Overseas trading took place between Western countries (Europe) and Eastern countries (Asia and the Middle East).	Overseas trade took place among several continents: _____
The main trading centres were European cities.	Trade also took place in distant lands known as _____
Merchants grew wealthy on the profits of trade.	Colonizers grew wealthy by profiting from _____ _____

8 Describe in your own words the "world economy" of the 16th century.

_____

_____

_____

SUMMARIZE WHAT YOU HAVE LEARNED

Using the following words, write a short text explaining how the very first "world economy" took shape during the Renaissance.

> colonization • lands • Age of Discovery • motive • colonial empire • trade • slave • culture • technology

_____

_____

_____

_____

_____

_____

_____

_____

RETURN TO THE SECTION "ON THE TRAIL"

Return to pages 36 and 37 and reread your answers to the questions. Reassess them in the light of what you have learned since. Then try to answer the two questions you wrote down on page 37. If you cannot, try to figure out why.

Discuss and Take a Stand

During the Renaissance, European powers established colonies in America, Africa and Asia. They traded with the people in these colonies. The trade was dominated by Europeans, though, who imposed their trading rules, their laws and their culture on the conquered peoples. Are economic and cultural relationships fair between different countries today?

TC Your teacher will give you a worksheet including questions and illustrations as clues. Try and answer the questions using the visual clues. Then discuss your answers with your classmates.

On the Trail

The society you live in guarantees individuals certain fundamental human rights. These rights include the right to express one's opinion, the right to practise the religion of one's choice, the right to private property and the right to live in security. In Canada, citizens who are 18 years old and over have the right to elect their leaders. These rights have not always been recognized. They were affirmed during revolutions that took place in the 17th and 18th centuries.

Look at the illustrations on these two pages and answer the questions.

Bloc Québécois MP Francine Lalonde has reopened the debate on assisted suicide ... She has tabled Bill C-407, An Act to Amend the Criminal Code (Right to Die with Dignity), which will be debated in the House of Commons in early November ... Inspired by laws passed in Europe and the United States, Francine Lalonde plans to change the Criminal Code to allow a doctor or any other person assisted by a doctor to "aid a person close to death or suffering from a debilitating illness to die with dignity if the person has expressed the free and informed wish to die."

Michel Vastel, "Le suicide assisté au Feuilleton" (Assisted Suicide on the Order Paper), *L'Actualité*, November 1, 2005. Free translation.

3.1 *The storming of the Bastille during the French Revolution, 1789.*

Do you know what human rights are being demanded in our society today?

_____

_____

_____

_____

_____

How could one go about demanding recognition for human rights?

_____

_____

_____

_____

_____

B先生，我亲爱的叔叔奥尔良公爵亲切地把你的这封信寄给你，告诉你我希望你确定哈罗埃特先生被带到我的巴士底城堡，并被拘留在那里。上帝保佑你，B先生。
路易斯先生.

Monsieur de B. I send you this letter by the kind hand of the Regent, my uncle the Duke of Orleans, to inform you that I would like you to make sure that Mr. Harrouët is taken into my castle of the Bastille, and detained there until further notice. God's blessings upon you, Monsieur de B.

Louis.

Order sent in the name of Louis XV, King of France, to imprison Mr. Harrouët (the philosopher Voltaire) in the Bastille prison, 1717. Free translation.

以法国国王路易十五世的名义寄出，在1717年在巴士底监狱监禁哈罗埃特先生.（摄 哲学家伏尔泰）.

3.2 *Louis XV, King of France from 1715 to 1774.*

3.3 *The Supreme Court of Canada.*

"主权在我身上，法院以我的名义作出公正的判决，所有的司法机关依然与我同在，对我来说，一个拥有立法权，对他人没有任何责任，也没有任何权力 由我分割。全部来自我，而国家的 权利和利益都在手中."

"Sovereign power resides in my person alone. The courts render justice in my name, and all judicial authority remains with me ... To me alone belongs all legislative power, with neither any responsibility to others nor any division of that power. Public order in all its entirety emanates from me, and the rights and interests of the nation ... rest only in my hands."

Declaration of Louis XV, King of France, 1766. From *A Concise History of France* by Roger Price. Cambridge University Press, 2005.

法国国王路易十五世的宣言，在1766年.《罗杰·普赖斯的法国简史》剑桥大学出版社.2005年.

Do you think human rights are more likely to be respected if there is one person in charge of justice? Explain your answer.

_____
_____
_____
_____
_____

Write down two more questions that come to mind about human rights.

• _____
_____
_____

• _____
_____
_____

At a Glance

What Was the Context of the French Revolution? 法国大革命的背景是什么？

As you learned in Inquiry 2, France was one of the four European kingdoms that conquered the world during the Renaissance. In this Inquiry you will find out how French society was organized in the 17th and 18th centuries, how philosophers disagreed with this form of social organization, and how it was finally overthrown by the Revolution in 1789.

正如你在 Inquiry 2 所学到的，法国是文艺复兴时期征服世界的四个欧洲王国之一。在这个调查中，您将了解17世纪和18世纪法国社会的组织方式，哲学家如何不同意，这种社会形17最推区

Social divisions in France

In the 17th and 18th centuries, French society was divided into three social groups known as "estates": the clergy, the nobility and the third estate (common people). 法国社会的分裂。

在七世纪和十八世纪，法国社会被划分为"地产"的社会群体。称为神职人员、贵族和第三产业(老百姓)

The clergy

The higher clergy were few in number. They lived in luxury and were members of the king's court. Many of them were from the nobility. The lower clergy consisted of parish priests, many of whom were from the third estate. Most lived a simple life in the countryside.

神职人员：更高的神职人员数量少，他们生活奢侈，是国王的成员，许多人来自贵族。下层的神职人员由教区牧师组成，其中许多人来自第三产业大。少数人在农村过简单的生活。

The nobility

贵族
贵族是地主。
他们没有业，
而是靠他们
的土地和皇室的津贴来生活。
贵族是世袭的，也就是说一个人的出身高贵。高贵的贵族
是国王的法庭成员。他们是皇室行政官员,是战时的军事指挥官。贵族较低的是在各省居住的土地所有者。

The nobility were the landowners. They did not work, but lived on the income from their land and from royal allowances. Nobility was hereditary, meaning that one was noble by birth. The upper nobility were members of the king's court. They were the royal administrators and were military commanders in time of war. The lower nobility were seigneurs who lived on their land in the provinces.

The third estate 第三地产

The third estate was made up of all those who were neither clergy nor nobility. Most were peasants, and lived in poverty. Bourgeois professionals such as merchants, bankers and lawyers were also members of the third estate. Those who could afford it could become noblemen by buying titles, and members of the third estate could improve their social status by becoming priests. They would then be in the lower clergy.

第三第产阶不是神职人员，也不是贵族。大多数是农民，生活贫困。商人，银行家，律师等专业人员也是第三地产的成员。通过购买头衔成为贵族，第三地产的成员可以通过成为牧师，来提高他们的社会地位，然后他们个会成为下层的神职人员。

3.4 THE THREE ESTATES

bourgeois

98% Third estate

peasant

Nobility 1.5% — — 0.5% Clergy

court: group of attendants to the monarch.
allowance: regular payment made to a person.

seigneur: noble landowner in France.
bourgeois: member of the French middle class, or town dwell

第三地产的成员的一个数字低于贵族或神职人员的数字；对同样的犯罪。

地产之间的不平等。

第三地和其他两个产业之间存在着广泛的社会不平等。只在第三地产的成员才需要交税；另外两个地产不在审判中。

Inequality among the estates

There were wide social inequalities between the third estate and the two others.

– Only members of the third estate were required to pay **taxes**; the other two estates were not;

– At a trial, the word of a member of the third estate counted for less than the word of a member of the nobility or the clergy;

– For an identical crime, members of the third estate were sentenced to harsher punishments, such as hanging, than members of the other two estates.

第三地产的成员比其它两个地产的成员被判处更严厉的惩罚，如绞挂。

Conflict between the bourgeoisie and the nobility

Members of the nobility did not work and took great pride in their **idleness**. They despised the third estate, whose members had to work for a living. They were fond of their privileges, and did not want any changes in the way society was organized.

On the other hand the bourgeoisie, who were members of the third estate, held work in high esteem. They objected to the fact that the nobility possessed social status, wealth and privilege simply because they were born to it, not because they had earned it.

3.5 ABSOLUTE MONARCHY UNDER LOUIS XIV

阶级和贵族之间的冲突：

们没有工作，对他们的闲散感到非常自豪。

们鄙视第三地产，他们的成员必须为谋生而工作。

们的特权，不想要任何东西社会组织方式的变化

方面，但为第三地产的资产阶级高度重视工作。他

对贵族拥有社会地位，财富和特权，仅仅是因为

们天生就是，不是因为他们已经 赢得了。

Absolute monarchy 绝对的君主制。

In the Middle Ages, the power of the king of France was limited by the power of the nobility, who possessed immense tracts of land. In the 16th century, King Francis I strengthened his royal power by withdrawing many of the nobility's privileges. His successors suppressed any attempts at rebellion among the nobility. The monarchy was at its most powerful during the reign of Louis XIV.

在中世纪法国国王的权力受到拥有大片土地的贵族的力量的限制

King Louis XIV, who reigned from 1643 to 1715, exercised absolute power in France. This absolute monarchy lasted until the late 18th century. Although the king surrounded himself with administrators, they were simply there to carry out his orders. He alone made all decisions concerning his kingdom. All inhabitants were the king's **subjects**. In theory, he had absolute control over them.

Kings were believed to rule by "divine right," in other words because they were chosen by God. When a king was crowned, the clergy confirmed his divine right to royal authority. In return, the king protected the interests of the Catholic Church. In practice, the monarchy was a hereditary office.

① 十六世纪，弗朗西斯一世国王通过撤销许多贵族的特权来增强他的皇权。他的继任者压制了任何在贵族叛乱中的企图。君主制在路易十四统治时期是最强大的。

② 国王路易十四统治于1643至1715年，在法国行使绝对的权力。这绝对的君主制一直持续到18世纪末。虽然，国王为行政官包围，他他们只是在那里执行命令。他独自一人做了有关他的王国的一切决定。

God

King

Chancellor and judicial council

Controller-General of Finances
Secretaries of State
King's Council

Intendants
(the king's representatives in the provinces)

Parlements
(registered royal edicts and served as courts)

---

tax: the money a government collects to pay for public expenses.

idleness: the state of not working and spending all one's time in recreation.

subject: a person who is under the authority of a king.

一切的权力，例如：

In this absolute monarchy, the king had all the powers, for example:
– the power to make laws;
– the power to levy taxes and collect them;
– the power to organize trade with the colonies;
– the power to imprison whomever he wanted, without explanation;
– the power to declare war and sign peace treaties;
– the power to impose the religion of his choice on the people.

French society in this era, based on the three estates and absolute monarchy, is known as the Ancien Régime. The Ancien Régime was abolished by the French Revolution in 1789.

Portrait of Louis XIV by Hyacinthe Rigaud, 1701.

LOUIS XIV (1638 to 1715)

Louis XIV, son of King Louis XIII, was crowned at the age of four and ruled in his own right from the age of 22. He established absolute monarchy in France. He was nicknamed "The Sun King" in recognition of his power.

Louis XIV made all the decisions concerning the kingdom. He recognized only the Roman Catholic Church. Protestants were persecuted. Many took refuge in other European countries or in America.

Louis XIV waged war against most other countries in Europe to expand French territory and gain supremacy throughout the continent. These wars were extremely expensive.

The king granted allowances to the nobility, maintained embassies abroad and threw huge parties. He built a luxurious palace at Versailles, where he lived from 1682 on. All the king's expenses were financed by taxes, which were paid by the third estate. No one in the kingdom had the power to control his spending.

✳ **3.6** *The Palace of Versailles.*

King Louis XIV hired the best artists, sculptors, architects and gardeners of his day to build this palace, which was to be a symbol of his power. The Palace of Versailles was the royal residence of Louis XIV and his successors until 1789.

3.7 THE AGE OF REVOLUTIONS

1751–72: Diderot and d'Alembert's *Encyclopedia, or Systematic Dictionary of the Sciences, Arts, and Crafts* (France)

1789: Beginning of the French Revolution; Declaration of the Rights of Man and of the Citizen

1689: Bill of Rights (England)

1688–89: English Revolution

France: Louis XIV

Russia: Peter the Great

Russia: Catherine II

MODERN TIMES	MODERN TIMES	MODERN TIMES	MODERN TIMES	MODERN TIMES	MODERN TIMES	MODERN TIMES	MODERN TIMES	CONTEMPORARY ERA

1600   1650   1700   1750   1800

Let's Get to Work!

1 Match each of the following statements with an estate of the Ancien Régime. Check the correct choice.

	CLERGY	NOBILITY	THIRD ESTATE
a) We are merchants.	○	○	✓
b) We do not pay taxes.	○	✓	✓
c) We are bourgeois members of the estate.	○	○	✓
d) We believe the king's authority comes from God.	✓	○	○
e) We make up the vast majority of the French population.	○	○	✓
f) We are peasants.	○	○	✓
g) We despise work.	○	✓	○
h) We are the privileged estates.	○	✓	✓

2 Which of the three estates do you think were able to influence the king? Why?

Nobility because they are members of the same family who share the same interests.

3 Look at the Palace of Versailles (figure 3.6, page 72), which was built for King Louis XIV. What are the clues telling you how powerful the king was?

The statues are sign of wealth and power. The home is massive. well looked after and huge amounts of land

4 In the 17th and 18th centuries France was an absolute monarchy. Look up "monarchy" and "absolute" in the dictionary, and then explain in your own words what the term "absolute monarchy" means.

a) Meaning of "monarchy": Rule by a King / Queen

b) Meaning of "absolute": Total, complete

c) Meaning of "absolute monarchy": Completely controlled by a King or a queen.

5 Do you think Louis XIV really had absolute control over every single one of his subjects? Explain your answer.

No, it's impossible for one person to know what is always going on.

(6) Find an example of how the king of France intervened in each of the following areas.

a) Economy: The power to levy taxes and collect them.

_____

b) Foreign policy: Start war or sign a pease treaty.

_____

c) Religion: The power to impose the religion of this choice.

_____

d) Justice: The power to make laws. the power to imprison. anyone for no reason.

_____

(7) a) Why did the king of France need a lot of money? Explain your answer.

To build lavish homes and throw wild parties. fight expensive wars. He had to pay allowances to his nobility.

_____

b) How did the king get all the money that he spent?

taxes.

c) Which estate would have been unhappy about this? Give reasons for your answer.

Third estate because they are the one's payings taxes.

(8) How was the king of France chosen? Check the right answer.

◯ He was chosen for his courage in war and for his military skills.

◯ He was chosen for his ability to administer the kingdom.

☑ He became king because he was the son or the descendant of the previous monarch.

(9) Describe society under the Ancien Régime in your own words.

_____

_____

_____

_____

(10) If you lived in France during the Ancien Régime and you were a member of the third estate, how would you like to change society? Give at least two answers.

• _____

_____

• _____

Project

We sometimes take for granted the rights and freedoms that we enjoy in our society. But we should not. Even in supposedly democratic Western societies, fundamental rights are sometimes violated. It is therefore the duty of every citizen to constantly defend our collective and individual rights and freedoms.

Task: In this Inquiry, we invite you to deepen your knowledge of a particular right or freedom, and to promote it.

Final product required: An informative advertisement that shows the importance of a right or a freedom in Quebec society today.

Several steps are necessary to complete the project. Use the Project Planning Guide TC that your teacher will give you.

1 Choose a freedom or a fundamental right. It might be freedom of thought, freedom of religion, or freedom of expression; or the right to security, the right to equality, or any other right or freedom you choose.

2 Collect information on your chosen right or freedom and formulate a definition.

3 Imagine what society was like before this freedom or this right was recognized. Design an advertisement that promotes your chosen freedom or right. Use advertisements that you find attractive or effective to help you design yours. Present it using information and communications technology (ICT). You might make a video, a poster or another type of presentation.

4 Evaluate the type of presentation you chose for your advertisement. Are you satisfied with it, or do you think another technique might have been more effective?

What Factors Led to the French Revolution?

While France was living under an absolute monarchy, England was setting up a monarchy in which the king shared power with representatives of the people. Many French philosophers were full of admiration for this political system, and wanted France to have a similar division of powers.

The beginning of parliamentary government

The king of England began sharing power with Parliament in about 1350. This Parliament had two parts:
- The House of Lords, made up of members of the higher clergy and the upper nobility;
- The House of Commons, made up of representatives of the lower nobility and the bourgeoisie.

The king did not have the right to levy taxes or raise an army without the approval of Parliament. It was the king who called Parliament to meet.

Parliament	King
Legislative powers (Making laws)	Executive powers (Enforcing the laws)

Members of Parliament

3.8 *The House of Commons, circa 1710.*

From the 14th to the 17th century, there was a power struggle between the members of Parliament and the king. The king tried to bypass Parliament by not calling it to meet, and he imprisoned members of Parliament who were opposed to him.

In 1679, Parliament passed a very important law guaranteeing every person a fundamental right: the right to justice. This law was called habeas corpus.

Did you know... Did you know... Did y

HABEAS CORPUS

Habeas corpus is a statement of the basic freedom not to be imprisoned without trial. This law requires that anyone who is arrested has the right to know why they are being arrested and what the charge is. They may then be released on **bail** and must be brought before a judge within three days.

This law, passed by the English Parliament in the 17th century, is still in force in many Western countries. It is sometimes suspended in exceptional circumstances, however, such as in wartime or during terrorist attacks.

Did you know... Did you know... Did y

 Can one be imprisoned without an explanation in Canada today?

In the 17th century, the philosopher John Locke (1632 to 1704) affirmed other rights, such as the right to property and freedom of thought. In his opinion, Parliament was more important than the king. He also believed that if the king did not respect the laws passed by Parliament, the people had the right to rise up against him and even overthrow him.

3.9 *Portrait of John Locke. Anonymous, 17th century.*

---

parliament: assembly with the power to make laws.

bail: sum of money paid by prisoners for their release until tried in court.

The English Revolution

In the late 17th century, King James II tried to establish an absolute monarchy modelled on the French system.

Parliament reacted to this threat by drafting the Bill of Rights, which set strict limits on the king's powers.

James II was overthrown and fled to the court of the King of France, Louis XIV.

Parliament offered the English throne to Mary, the king's eldest daughter, and her husband William of Orange, on condition that they both agree to the Bill of Rights. They consented, and Parliament appointed them King and Queen of England.

Below are some clauses from the Bill of Rights, passed by English Parliament in 1689:

> "Lords Spiritual and Temporal and Commons, ... for the vindicating and asserting of their ancient rights and liberties, [do] declare:
>
> 1. That the pretended power of suspending the laws or the execution of laws by regal authority without consent of Parliament is illegal;
>
> 2. That levying money ... without grant of Parliament ... is illegal;
>
> 3. That it is the right of the subjects to petition the king, and all ... prosecutions for such petitioning are illegal;
>
> 4. That the raising or keeping of a standing army within the kingdom in time of peace, unless it be with consent of Parliament, is against law;
>
> 5. That election of members of Parliament ought to be free;
>
> 6. That the freedom of speech ... in Parliament ought not to be impeached or questioned in any court;
>
> 7. And that for redress of all grievances, and for the amending, strengthening and preserving of the laws, Parliaments ought to be held frequently."
>
> Bill of Rights, 1689.

The English Revolution, which took place without any bloodshed, was very significant because:
– monarchs would now be appointed by Parliament: their power would come from Parliament and not from God;
– monarchs no longer had absolute power: they had to respect habeas corpus and the Bill of Rights.

The 1689 Revolution established a parliamentary monarchy in England.

3.10 ENGLISH PARLIAMENTARY MONARCHY IN THE 17TH CENTURY

Legislative powers   **Executive powers**

Parliament ← approves — King or Queen

House of Lords

House of Commons

King or Queen → approves → Cabinet: Prime Minister, Ministers

House of Commons → chooses → Cabinet

Wealthy landowners → elect → House of Commons

3.11 *Prime Minister Tony Blair and Queen Elizabeth II in 2005. Parliamentary monarchy is still the political system in Great Britain today.*

revolution: overthrow of the social order, often starting as a revolt against the established authority.

Let's Get to Work!

1 a) Locate the three following events leading to a change in England's political system on the timeline below.

1. English Parliament established
2. Habeas corpus passed
3. Bill of Rights declared

Write the years under the timeline at 100-year intervals.

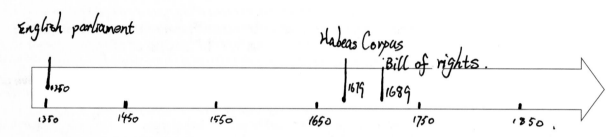

English parliament

Habeas Corpus
Bill of rights.

1350   1679   1689

1350   1450   1550   1650   1750   1850.

b) Which of the three events on your timeline marks the beginning of parliamentary monarchy in England?

Bill of rights.

2 a) What do you call the powers
   1. to make laws? _Legislative Power_
   2. to enforce laws? _executive powers_

b) Who holds legislative powers
   1. in an absolute monarchy? _the King_
   2. in a parliamentary monarchy? _Parliament_

c) Who holds executive powers
   1. in an absolute monarchy? _King_
   2. in a parliamentary monarchy? _King_

3 Look at the diagram showing absolute monarchy in France under Louis XIV (figure 3.5, page 71).

a) In the diagram, which way are all the arrows pointing?

All arrows are pointining down.

b) What do you think this means?

The power goes from the top to the bottom.

4 Now look at the diagram showing English parliamentary monarchy (figure 3.10, page 77).

a) Why aren't all the arrows in the diagram pointing down?

Because the power is shared amongst many different people.

b) What does the green arrow pointing upwards mean, in the diagram?

Wealithy landowners elect representatives.

c) What new right does this arrow represent?

The right to elect you leader.

5 a) Look at the picture of the House of Commons (figure 3.8, page 76). What do you notice about the number of people who exercised power in England in the 17th century?

There are many people who share power

b) In the same era, how was the exercise of power in France different from this?

Only the King has the power.

6 How were members of the House of Commons chosen in the 17th century?
Check the correct answer.

◯ They were elected by all the inhabitants of England.

☑ They were elected by the wealthy landowners of England.

◯ They were chosen by the king or queen.

7 Read the following passage and answer the questions.

"The sheriff who has the prisoner in his keeping must bring him before a judge within three days ... He must then inform him of the reason for his detention."

a) From which law do you think this passage is taken?

Habeas Corpus

b) From what you have learned, what rights does this law guarantee?

The right to be before a judge, the right to know why you're being arrested. The right to bail.

c) What do you think might have been the situation in England before this law was passed?

People went to jail for no reason Parliament.

d) Who passed this law? Check the correct answer.

◯ The king   ◯ The people

◯ The courts   ☑ Parliament

Inquiry 3 The French Revolution   **79**

8 The following questions are about how parliamentary monarchy worked in the 17th century. Answer yes or no to the questions. Use a clause from the Bill of Rights to support each of your answers (see page 77).

a) Could the king try to influence the election of Parliament?

◯ Yes   ☑ No

Supporting clause: _____ #5 _____

_____

b) Could members of Parliament say what they thought?

☑ Yes   ◯ No

Supporting clause: _____ #6 _____

_____

c) Could the king decide to levy a tax, for example to pay for his wars?

◯ Yes   ☑ No

Supporting clause: _____ #2 _____

_____

9 a) Why was King James II overthrown?

He tried to establish an absolute monarchy.

b) Why do you think William and Mary agreed to sign the Bill of Rights?

Because they wanted to be king and queen.

10 From what you now know, how will the following people be chosen?

a) The next monarch of England: _Hereditary goes from mother/father to son/daughter._

b) The next prime minister of England: _election._

11 Explain in your own words the difference between absolute monarchy and parliamentary monarchy by completing the following sentences.

a) In an absolute monarchy, _Absolute Monarchy. The king has ali the power. He shares with NOBODY_

b) In a parliamentary monarchy, _Parliamentary monarchy The king and the Parliament share the power._

12 In your opinion, did the parliamentary monarchy of 1689 have any of the characteristics of a democracy? Explain your answer.

Yes. because the parliament is made up of elected people.
No. because the King IS NOT. elected.

The philosophy of the Enlightenment

In the 18th century, philosophers in France and other European countries admired the English political system and questioned the system of absolute monarchy.

Like the humanists who preceded them, these philosophers believed in progress. They thought that this progress could be achieved through reason, education, tolerance and freedom. They hoped that reason would "enlighten" society and would help it progress towards happiness.

These philosophers had such a powerful influence on 18th-century society that the era itself is known as "The Enlightenment."

Enlightenment philosophers not only affirmed individual rights and freedoms, but also collective rights. This affected the way society was politically organized.

The right to choose one's leaders

In France in the 18th century, the king had supreme authority over all the inhabitants of the kingdom. Every person was his subject, and had no right to participate in public life.

Enlightenment philosophers rejected the notion of the "subject" and introduced the notion of the "citizen." Every citizen was equal and free, and could take part in public life.

Philosopher Jean-Jacques Rousseau believed that all the citizens of a country should freely choose their own political system. They should also have the right to replace leaders who acted in their own interests rather than for the common good.

The separation of powers

In every society there are three kinds of powers:
– legislative powers (making laws)
– executive powers (enforcing the laws)
– judicial powers (judging those accused of breaking the laws).

In an absolute monarchy, the king himself holds all three kinds of powers. The philosopher Montesquieu believed that this situation led to injustices, and he demanded that the three powers be separated. This demand was inspired by the ideas of English philosopher John Locke.

✳ JEAN-JACQUES ROUSSEAU (1712 TO 1778)

Philosopher Jean-Jacques Rousseau belonged to the French bourgeoisie.

He believed that power should belong to all citizens, who should choose what kind of political system they wanted. Not everyone could be in the government, of course, so the people should make an agreement with their chosen leaders as to how they wanted to be governed.

> "[I consider] the establishment of the body politic as a true contract between a people and the leaders they choose, a contract by which both parties commit themselves to observe the laws that are spelled out in its articles and that form the bonds of their union."
>
> Jean-Jacques Rousseau, *Discourse on the Origin of Inequality*, 1755. Translated by Franklin Philip. Oxford Paperbacks, 1999.

Portrait of Jean-Jacques Rousseau by Maurice Quentin de La Tour, 1753.

---

public life: influence or authority in the political system.

Freedom of religion

In the 18th century, Catholicism was the only faith the king permitted in France. Protestants were persecuted.

Enlightenment philosophers accused the Catholic clergy of keeping people in ignorance and religious fanaticism.

They thought that people of all faiths should be accepted as equals. Many of these philosophers were deists. Deists believed in the existence of a supreme Being who did not intervene in human affairs.

The philosopher Voltaire was a strong advocate of religious tolerance.

Freedom of thought and freedom of expression

Freedom of thought and freedom of expression meant that people could publicly criticize the established political system without fear of being arrested. Freedom of expression went hand in hand with freedom of the press.

Other rights

- Enlightenment philosophers were against torture.
- They believed that prisoners should have the possibility of pardon.
- They wanted education to be widely available so that technological and scientific knowledge could progress.

 FRANÇOIS MARIE AROUET, KNOWN AS VOLTAIRE (1694 TO 1778)

Voltaire was the son of a lawyer and came from a bourgeois background. He wrote many books, including dictionaries and plays.

In 1726, he was sent to jail for insulting a nobleman. When he was released he spent three years in England, and absorbed many of the ideas of English philosopher John Locke.

Voltaire spent his life speaking out against religious intolerance and against the wars that it caused. He thought the ideal religion was deism.

Voltaire was from the bourgeoisie, and shared bourgeois values. He made fun of the nobility, whom he thought were useless members of society, as the following passage shows:

> "I, however, do not know which is the more useful to the State: a nobleman in a powdered wig who knows exactly when the king arises and when he retires, and who gives himself airs of greatness ... or a merchant who enriches his country, who sends orders from his counting house to Surat and Cairo, and contributes to the well-being of the world."
>
> Voltaire, *Philosophical Letters, Or, Letters Regarding the English Nation*, 1743. Edited by John Leigh, translated by Prudence Steiner. Indianapolis, IN: Hackett Publishing Co., 2007.

Portrait of Voltaire. École française, 1775.

merchant: trader who is involved in international commerce.

The spread of Enlightenment ideas

Enlightenment philosophers used many techniques for spreading their ideas:

- publishing journals, pamphlets and posters;

- holding meetings in private living rooms and in cafés;

- publishing many books, which were very popular among the bourgeoisie (dictionaries, philosophical treatises, plays, novels, etc.).

3.12 *Freedom of the press. Engraving, 1795.*

The spread of Enlightenment ideas gave rise to a new phenomenon: public opinion. The bourgeoisie talked about these new ideas in the streets and cafés. Public opinion was generally in favour of the Enlightenment, but the nobility and the king were against the new ideas. Philosopher Denis Diderot was imprisoned for several months. Voltaire and Rousseau had to flee France and take refuge abroad on several occasions. Diderot's *Encyclopedia* was printed in the Netherlands and in England, but had to be introduced into France secretly because the king had forbidden its publication.

✳THE *ENCYCLOPEDIA* (1751–72)

In 1751, mathematician Jean le Rond D'Alembert and philosopher Denis Diderot published a massive encyclopedia.

Made up of 17 books of text and 11 books of plates, the *Encyclopedia or Dictionary of the Sciences and the Arts* was an attempt to collect together all the knowledge that had been acquired in every field to date: science and technology, agriculture, crafts, religion, politics, etc.

About 50 key figures, including artists, intellectuals and writers, contributed to the *Encyclopedia*. Its publication took 21 years.

The authors of the *Encyclopedia* wrote articles about politics and society that communicated the ideas of the Enlightenment. The *Encyclopedia* was condemned by the Catholic Church as dangerous, and banned by the king. Nevertheless, 25,000 copies were printed and it was translated into several languages.

The following is from an article by Denis Diderot called "Political Authority."

> "No man has by nature been granted the right to command others. Liberty is a gift from heaven, and every member of the same species has the right to enjoy it as soon as he is in possession of reason ... On close examination, [authority] can always be traced back to one of two sources: either the strength and violence of the person who has got hold of it, or the consent of those who have submitted themselves to it, by virtue of a contract, actual or presumed, with the person on whom they have conferred it."

Encyclopedia or Dictionary of the Sciences and the Arts, 1751–72.
From *Political Writings*, translated by J. Hope Mason and R. Wokler.
Cambridge University Press, 1992.

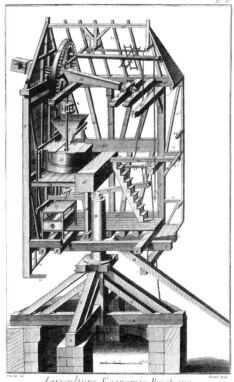

Agriculture. Economic Rustique
Moulin à Vent

Windmill machinery. Plate from the Encyclopedia.

What are the differences between Diderot's 18th-century *Encyclopedia* and encyclopedias today?

Let's Get to Work!

1. Explain each of the following fundamental freedoms in your own words.

   a) Freedom of religion: _____

   The right to choose your religion and practice it freely.

   b) Freedom of expression: _____

   The right to speak your opinion without fear of being arrested

2. a) Were the freedoms in question 1) recognized in France during the Ancien Régime? ___ *No.*

   b) Give two justifications for your answer.

   • *The king would arrest you if you disagreed with him.*

   • *The king chose the religion of his kingdom.*

3. The Enlightenment philosophers were critical of absolute monarchy and the privileges of the nobility. To which of the three estates of society in the Ancien Régime do you think most of them belonged?

   3rd Estate

4. The philosopher Montesquieu advocated the principle of the separation of powers. Demonstrate your knowledge of the separation of powers by following the instructions below.

   a) Match each set of powers with its definition.

   1. Legislative powers   Enforcing the laws

   2. Executive powers   Judging those who are accused of breaking the laws

   3. Judicial powers   Making the laws

   b) In the passage by Montesquieu below, highlight

   1. The part that describes legislative powers in yellow;

   2. The part that describes executive powers in blue;

   3. The part that describes judicial powers in pink.

   "In each state there are three sorts of powers ... By the first, the prince or the magistrate makes laws for a time or for always and corrects or abrogates those that have been made. By the second, he makes peace or war, sends or receives embassies, establishes security, and prevents invasions. By the third, he punishes crimes or judges disputes between individuals."

   Montesquieu, *The Spirit of the Laws*, 1748. From *Cambridge Texts in the History of Political Thought*, translated and edited by A.M. Cohler, B.C. Miller and H.S. Stone. Cambridge University Press, 1989.

5. a) How did the ideas of the Enlightenment philosophers spread?

   Newspaper, books, coffee shops, letter, talking etc...

b) Were these methods similar to the methods the humanists used to spread their ideas in 16th-century Europe?

Yes .

c) Are they similar to methods of spreading ideas nowadays?

Yes and no. We still have newspapers. and write letters, but we also have the internet .

6 Between the *Encyclopedia* and the newspapers, which of the two methods of spreading ideas

a) was most accessible to the poor? _a newspapers_

b) explained Enlightenment ideas in most detail? _Encyclopedia ._

7 While a prisoner in France, the hero of a short story by Voltaire makes the following statement:

> "There is no rule of law at all in this country! We condemn men without giving them a hearing. It is not like this in England."
>
> Voltaire, *l'Ingénu*, 1767. Free translation.

a) Is it true that in Voltaire's France someone could be imprisoned without trial?

Yes .

b) In England in the same era, which law protected people against imprisonment without trial?

Habeas Corpus

c) In what year was this law passed?

_1679_

d) How do you think the king of France reacted to the publication of Voltaire's short story *l'Ingénu*?

He didn't like it and he probably banned it .

e) Explain in your own words the impact of the English Revolution on Enlightenment ideas.

The English had a parliamentary monarchy. They had the habeas corpus, and finally they had the bill of rights.

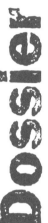
What Was the French Revolution?

Under the influence of the Enlightenment philosophers, more and more people began to question absolute monarchy. Meanwhile other factors, too, contributed to ending it.

The financial crisis

As you read earlier, the king of France spent vast sums of money.

From 1786 onwards, France's finances were a disaster. Many expensive wars had emptied the treasury. Expenditures were far higher than revenues.

King Louis XVI, who had been on the throne since 1774, could not borrow any more from the banks, as 50% of his spending already went to repaying his debts. His other source of income was taxes, a burden that the third estate carried entirely alone.

Income

Taxes

Expenses
- Wars
- Diplomatic missions abroad
- Allowances for nobility, lavish parties
- Helping the poor (charity, public welfare costs etc.)
- Paying back the debt

3.13 *Cartoon showing the three estates during the Ancien Régime.*

The agricultural crisis

The vast majority of the French population were peasants. Although they were the poorest, they were the most heavily taxed. They had to pay **tithes** to the Catholic Church to support the priests. They also had to pay taxes on salt, a head tax (a tax on simply existing!), a window tax, and many others. They had to give days of unpaid labour, or *corvées*, to the seigneur. All these seigneurial obligations dated back to the Middle Ages.

In 1787 and 1788, two bad harvests in a row increased the poverty of the peasants and the urban lower classes.

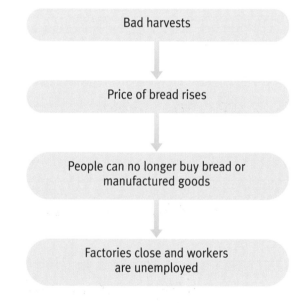

Bad harvests

↓

Price of bread rises

↓

People can no longer buy bread or manufactured goods

↓

Factories close and workers are unemployed

Seigneurs **stockpiled** wheat and resold it for a fortune. Peasants and the urban poor revolted. Riots broke out. People made accusations against
- the rich, for growing wealthy at the peasants' expense by trading in food;
- seigneurs, for using their ancestral rights to reduce the peasants to poverty.

tithe: a tenth of the annual agricultural produce given in support of the clergy.
stockpile: to gather a large supply of valuable goods.

The calling of the Estates-General

King Louis XVI feared an uprising, and considered taxing the nobility to solve the financial crisis. When the nobility refused to give up their privileges, he decided to consult deputies, or representatives, from all three estates.

The king called the Estates-General at the beginning of 1789. Among the members of the third estate, it was only the rich who were allowed to elect deputies. Elections were held in every region in France.

The Estates-General met on May 5, 1789. There were 1,139 deputies:
- 291 representing the clergy, mostly parish priests;
- 270 representing the nobility;
- 578 representing the third estate, almost all of them bourgeois businessmen and lawyers.

As they represented 98% of the population, deputies from the third estate demanded that each vote be equal, instead of weighted according to estate, as was the custom. The other two estates saw the third estate's determination, and agreed.

The king hoped that the Estates-General would solve France's financial crisis. The third estate believed the problem would be solved if the nobility and the clergy paid taxes. The two higher estates continued to refuse to pay them.

Deputies from the third estate were disappointed by the inflexible attitude of the nobility and the clergy. Aware of the support of the people, who were protesting in every region of France, the deputies demanded that France draw up a constitution. A clash between the third estate and the two privileged estates was now imminent.

3.14 *The Tennis Court Oath.*
On June 20, 1789, in a hall next to Versailles called the *Jeu de paume* (indoor tennis court), the deputies of the third estate vowed not to disband until they had drawn up a constitution for France.

LISTS OF GRIEVANCES

Members of the three estates throughout France saw the meetings of the Estates-General as an opportunity to draw up lists of grievances, or complaints. About 60,000 of these lists, known as *Cahiers de doléances*, were sent to the deputies of the Estates-General to be presented to the king.

These lists give us valuable insight into the thoughts of members of each of the estates of the Ancien Régime.

Many of the lists, drafted by members of the bourgeoisie and the peasantry, complained that the privileges of the nobility were the cause of all their problems.

"It is we poor villagers who must pay for cannons, guns, barracks, dishes, roads, all the while knowing that our children can never hold positions of military command. The door is closed to them. Nor can they ever hope to attain the higher ranks of the Church. All these special privileges are granted only to the nobility."

Excerpt from the *Cahier du tiers état des Essarts-le-Vicomte* (List of Grievances of the Essarts-le-Vicomte Third Estate), 1789. Free translation.

Estates-General: assembly of representatives of the three estates in the Ancien Régime.

constitution: fundamental law defining the structure of a government.

Name: .... Group: .... Date: ....

Let's Get to Work!

1 Why do you think the king of France had such a large debt to pay back?

Because he spent broe of money on wars, allowances and lavish parties.

2 Suggest two solutions to the financial problems of France in 1786.

- ____
- ____

3 Look at figure 3.13 on page 86.

a) Which person represents the third estate? ____________________

b) What is this cartoon saying?

____

c) Do you think that the artist was in favour of the social system of the Ancien Régime?

____

4 Were all three estates fairly represented at the Estates-General of 1789? To answer the question, follow the instructions below.

a) Use the percentages given on page 70 (figure 3.4) to show the size of each of the three estates on this grid. Each square represents 1%. Use a different colour for each estate, then colour in the key.

A. Percentage of the population from each estate

	1	2	3	4	5	6	7	8	9	10
1										
2										
3										
4										
5										
6										
7										
8										
9										
10										

Key

- ☐ Clergy
- ☐ Nobility
- ☐ Third estate

b) Now use the figures given on page 87 to calculate the percentage of deputies at the Estates-General representing each estate. Show your calculations.

1. Clergy: ____________________
2. Nobility: ____________________
3. Third estate: ____________________

c) Show the percentages you calculated in part b) by filling in the grid below, and colour in the key.

B. Percentage of each estate represented at the Estates-General

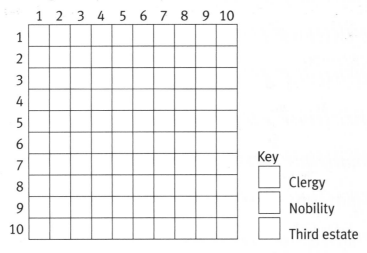

Key
- Clergy
- Nobility
- Third estate

d) What do you notice when you compare grids **A** and **B**?

_____

_____

_____

5 At the Estates-General, the three estates made several demands on the king.

a) What do you think the demands of the bourgeoisie would have been?

_____

b) What do you think the demands of the peasants would have been?

_____

_____

c) What do you think the demands of the clergy and the nobility would have been?

_____

6 a) What kind of political system usually involves electing representatives?

○ Monarchy   ○ Oligarchy

○ Democracy   ○ Empire

b) Do you think France had this kind of system in the 18th century? Explain your answer.

_____

_____

_____

_____

_____

The abolition of the monarchy

The series of events that was unleashed by the meeting of the Estates–General in 1789 is known as the French Revolution, and resulted in the abolition of the monarchy in France.

 Do you know what France's motto is today? Do you know the date of France's national holiday? Do you know its national anthem? What is its message?

3.15 THE FRENCH REVOLUTION

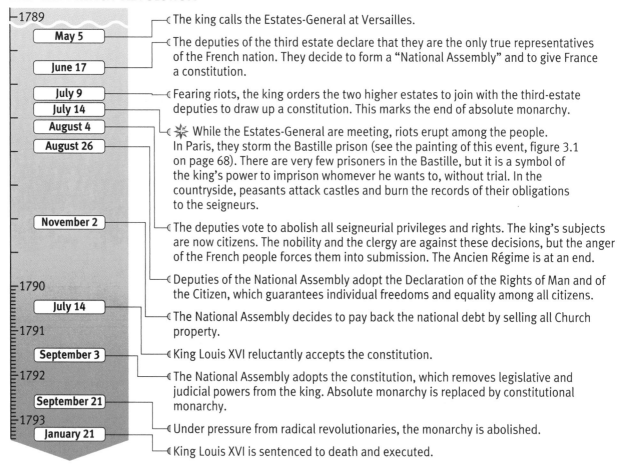

1789

May 5 — The king calls the Estates-General at Versailles.

June 17 — The deputies of the third estate declare that they are the only true representatives of the French nation. They decide to form a "National Assembly" and to give France a constitution.

July 9 — Fearing riots, the king orders the two higher estates to join with the third-estate deputies to draw up a constitution. This marks the end of absolute monarchy.

July 14

August 4 — ✳ While the Estates-General are meeting, riots erupt among the people. In Paris, they storm the Bastille prison (see the painting of this event, figure 3.1 on page 68). There are very few prisoners in the Bastille, but it is a symbol of the king's power to imprison whomever he wants to, without trial. In the countryside, peasants attack castles and burn the records of their obligations to the seigneurs.

August 26

November 2 — The deputies vote to abolish all seigneurial privileges and rights. The king's subjects are now citizens. The nobility and the clergy are against these decisions, but the anger of the French people forces them into submission. The Ancien Régime is at an end.

1790 — Deputies of the National Assembly adopt the Declaration of the Rights of Man and of the Citizen, which guarantees individual freedoms and equality among all citizens.

July 14 — The National Assembly decides to pay back the national debt by selling all Church property.

1791

September 3 — King Louis XVI reluctantly accepts the constitution.

1792 — The National Assembly adopts the constitution, which removes legislative and judicial powers from the king. Absolute monarchy is replaced by constitutional monarchy.

September 21

1793 — Under pressure from radical revolutionaries, the monarchy is abolished.

January 21 — King Louis XVI is sentenced to death and executed.

The French Revolution was followed by several decades of political turbulence.

A series of different political systems followed the Revolution, including an empire led by Napoleon Bonaparte. In the 19th century, France chose to become a republic, which is the system still in place today.

Research Mandate

Napoleon Bonaparte is a legendary figure in French history. What did he accomplish? Did he defend human rights? Do some research to find out.

3.16 *Execution of King Louis XVI.*

The guillotine, a heavy blade used to behead a convict, was introduced during the French Revolution. It was considered more humane than execution with an axe. Thousands of opponents of the French Revolution were guillotined.

republic: in France, a form of government in which the three powers are separated and the leader is elected.

The Declaration of the Rights of Man and of the Citizen

On August 26, 1789, the National Assembly adopted the Declaration of the Rights of Man and of the Citizen. It was inspired by the achievements of the English Revolution in the 17th century, as well as by the ideas of the Enlightenment. Democratic nations still follow the principles it laid down to this day. Here are a few excerpts:

"The Representatives of the French people, organized in National Assembly ... have resolved to set forth in a solemn declaration the natural, inalienable, and sacred rights of man ... In consequence, the National Assembly recognizes and declares, in the presence and under the auspices of the Supreme Being, the following rights of man and citizen:

Article 1. Men are born free and remain free and equal in rights ...

Article 2. The aim of every political association is the preservation of the natural and imprescriptible rights of man. These rights are liberty, property, security, and resistance to oppression.

Article 4. Liberty consists in the power to do anything that does not injure others ...

Article 6. Law is the expression of the general will. All citizens have the right to take part personally, or by their representatives, in its formation. It must be the same for all, whether it protects or punishes ...

Article 7. No man can be accused, arrested, or detained, except in the cases determined by the law ...

Article 10. No one should be disturbed on account of his opinions, even religious, provided their manifestation does not upset the public order established by law.

Article 11. The free communication of ideas and opinions is one of the most precious of the rights of man; every citizen can then speak, write, and print freely ...

Article 13. A general tax is indispensable for the maintenance of the public force and for the expenses of administration; it ought to be equally apportioned among all citizens according to their means."

Declaration of the Rights of Man and of the Citizen, 1789. From *The Constitutions and Other Select Documents Illustrative of the History of France, 1789–1907*, edited by Frank Maloy Anderson. New York: Russell and Russell, 1908.

The Declaration of the Rights of Man and of the Citizen did not apply to women or to inhabitants of French colonies. Women did not have the right to vote or to participate in public life. The practice of slavery continued in the colonies. It was banned in 1794, but restored a few years later. It was not abolished definitively until 1848.

The consequences of the French Revolution

- Abolition of the three estates
- Abolition of privileges for the clergy and nobility
- Abolition of all seigneurial rights
- Idea of subject replaced by idea of citizen
- Separation of powers
- Male citizens who worked and paid taxes had the right to vote
- Abolition of the monarchy

3.17 *Eugène Delacroix*, Liberty Leading the People, *1830.*

The feminine figure symbolizes liberty and the tricolor flag symbolizes the French Republic. Eugène Delacroix himself appears in the painting as a revolutionary (the man in the hat with a gun). This painting was inspired by another French revolution in 1830. The painting has come to symbolize all revolutions.

Let's Get to Work!

1 Seigneurial rights were abolished with the French Revolution. The seigneurial obligations of peasants dated from what era?

Middle Ages

2 What solution did the 1789 National Assembly come up with for solving France's financial problems?

The church property

3 Why did the king accept the constitution in 1790, even though it restricted his power?

He was aft afraid of riots and getting killed.

4 Match each of the following statements with an article from the Declaration of the Rights of Man and of the Citizen (see page 91).

a) Every man can participate in making laws. _____ 6

b) Every man must pay taxes, according to his means. _____ 13

c) All men are equal. _____ 1

d) One person's freedom ends where another's begins. _____ 4

e) Every man is free to practise the religion of his choice. _____ 10

f) The law applies to everyone. _____ 6

g) No one can be imprisoned without a reason. _____ 7

h) Every man has the right to own property. _____ 2

i) Newspapers may criticize the government. _____ 11

5 Write down an example of a common everyday situation in which the articles of the Declaration of the Rights of Man and of the Citizen are not respected.

a) Article 2: _____

_____

b) Article 4: _____

_____

6 Look at the painting in figure 3.17 on page 91 and read the passage underneath it. Do you think the artist was in favour of revolutionary ideas? Give reasons for your answer.

For the revolution. She is holding up the flag from the revolution and is standing proud.

_____

_____

_____

7 a) Name three acts of violence that were committed during the French Revolution.

- Riots
- storming of the bastille
- guillotine

b) Do you think the violence was necessary? Explain your answer.

Yes, because the people wouldn't have been taken seriously or heard without the violence.
No, in England they went through a ~~sm~~ similar revolution and not one person died. Violence is not the answer.

8 In the Declaration of the Rights of Man and of the Citizen (see page 91), name three rights or freedoms that were also affirmed by the Enlightenment philosophers.

- Freedom of speech   Equality   Freedom of expression.
- Freedom to own property
- Freedom of religion
  Freedom of the press

9 Find the words that match the following definitions.

a) A law that defines the structure of a government.

Constitution.

b) A representative of one of the three estates at the Estates-General.

Deputy

c) A political system in which the power of the king is limited by the constitution.

Constitutional monarchy.

d) What one can do, what a society allows.

Freedom or Right.

e) A person who participates in public life and is not the subject of a monarch.

Citizen

f) An uprising of the people against the government.

Revolution.

10 Number the following events in chronological order.

6	Louis XVI sentenced to death
3	Privileges of the Ancien Régime abolished
4	Declaration of the Rights of Man and of the Citizen
5	Adoption of a constitution
2	Rioting
1	Meeting of the Estates-General

How Was Russia Governed?

In the 18th century, Russia's population was around 25 million, about the same as France's. The population included peoples of many cultures and languages. Russia's immense territory covered parts of Europe and Asia. Its economy was based on agriculture and mining, and its strength lay in its army and navy.

Social groups

In the 18th century, Russia was ruled by a tsar. The tsar was the supreme leader of the country, as was the king in France under the Ancien Régime. Russian society was divided into three social classes:
– the clergy
– the nobility
– the rest of the population, mostly peasants.

The nobility were the landowners. They helped the tsar run the country and served in the military. Peasants were bonded to the nobleman's lands on which they lived. Their status, known as serfdom, resembled slavery. Although landowners did not have the power of life and death over their serfs, they could buy, sell and trade them. Peasants could not marry without their master's permission and could not leave his land.

3.18 **RUSSIA IN THE 18TH CENTURY**

✹ ST. PETERSBURG

Tsar Peter the Great (1672 to 1725) ruled Russia from 1682 to 1725. After travelling extensively around Europe, he returned with the idea of modernizing his country. He opened schools and reformed the state administration.

He founded the city of St. Petersburg in 1703. The French and Italian architects he hired used a highly geometrical design. In 1715, Peter the Great moved his capital from Moscow to St. Petersburg.

✹ *The Winter Palace, St. Petersburg.*

This palace is now the Hermitage Museum, which houses one of the largest collections of paintings in the world.

✳ **3.19** *Petrodvorets Palace, built by Tsar Peter the Great in the 18th century.*

Peter the Great built his imperial residence near St. Petersburg. He based its design on the Palace of Versailles, which he had visited. Petrodvorets Palace is surrounded by gardens with numerous statues and fountains, and is a lavish display of the power of the tsars.

Enlightened despotism

While the French were living under an absolute monarchy, many European sovereigns, including the Russian tsar, were attracted to the ideas of the Enlightenment. Although they were absolute monarchs, they were **enlightened despots** who attempted to make decisions based on reason.

Enlightened despots of the 18th century included:
– Gustav III of Sweden;
– Joseph II and Maria Theresa of Austria;
– Frederick II of Prussia;
– Catherine II of Russia.

Some of these enlightened despots, including Catherine II, **Tsarina** of Russia, corresponded regularly with the Enlightenment philosophers and invited them to their palaces.

Catherine II was interested in the writings of the Enlightenment philosophers. She read Montesquieu and corresponded with D'Alembert, Diderot and Voltaire. She had modern ideas and believed in developing her country's culture and industries. She encouraged scientists and opened schools. In 1766, inspired by Enlightenment ideas, she drafted a new code of law for Russia that would separate the three powers, abolish serfdom and ban torture and the death penalty.

In spite of her apparent interest in the Enlightenment, however, Catherine II had an authoritarian personality and behaved like an absolute monarch. Under her rule the situation of the peasants worsened. Serfdom increased, the nobility acquired more rights over the peasants and peasant uprisings were savagely put down. The drafting of the code of law was halted in 1768, and the code was never put into practice.

✳ **CATHERINE II OF RUSSIA (1729 TO 1796)**

Born a German princess, the young Sophie von Anhalt-Zerbst was the chosen wife of Peter III, heir to the Russian throne.

She took an immediate interest in her new country. She learned Russian, converted to Orthodox Christianity and adopted the Russian name Catherine. Peter, also from Germany, stayed a German at heart and never adapted to Russian life. Catherine was much more popular than he was, and when he became tsar she had her husband arrested by the Imperial Russian Guard and took control of the country.

Catherine II reigned for 34 years, from 1762 to 1796. Her foreign policy was one of conquest. By the time she died she had increased her territory by one third, and Russia had become a major world power.

Portrait of Tsarina Catherine II by F.S. Rokotov, circa 1770.

---

enlightened despot: absolute monarch who believes in the principles of the Enlightenment.

tsarina: feminine of tsar.

Name: .... Group: .... Date: ....

Let's Get to Work!

1 a) Look at the palaces of Petrodvorets (figure 3.19, page 95) and Versailles (figure 3.6, page 72). What message do they convey? Check the right answer or answers.

- ◯ Equality
- ◯ Power
- ◯ Freedom
- ◯ Wealth
- ◯ Democracy

b) Why do you think Peter the Great's visit to Versailles inspired him to build a similar kind of palace?

____

____

2 a) Fill out the table below, matching each social class in Russia with its equivalent estate in France during the Ancien Régime.

Social classes in Russia	Estates in France during the Ancien Régime
The clergy	______________________
The nobility	______________________
The peasants	______________________

b) What strikes you about the table?

____

____

3 Draw a diagram showing the social hierarchy under the tsars.

Let's Get to Work!

4 Using the following definitions, fill in the acrostic below to find the name of a person who played an important role in Russian history.

1. Synonym for a king or queen
2. Supreme leader of Russia
3. Synonym for an absolute sovereign
4. The original first name of the mystery person
5. City built by Peter the Great
6. Status of the Russian peasants
7. Russian social class
8. Intellectual movement of the 18th century
9. French philosopher

5 Why do you think Princess Sophie von Anhalt Erbst was chosen as the wife of the future tsar of Russia? Check the right answer.

◯ Because she was pretty ◯ Because she was from a noble family ◯ Because she was intelligent

6 The reign of Catherine II was full of contradictions. On the one hand, she admired the philosophers of the Enlightenment; on the other hand, she behaved like an absolute monarch. Show this contradiction by answering the following questions.

a) Which of Catherine II's actions showed she was open to the ideas of the Enlightenment?

_____

_____

_____

b) Which of her actions revealed that she tended towards absolute monarchy?

_____

_____

7 Why do you think Catherine II was so popular among the Russians?

_____

_____

Synthesis Activities

1. Look at this cartoon from 1787. It shows the three estates in French society during the Ancien Régime.

   a) Write down the name of the estate that each person represents.

   b) Explain in your own words what this cartoon is criticizing.

   _____

   _____

   _____

2. Explain in your own words the following characteristics of the English political system in the 17th century.

   a) The separation of powers: _____

   _____

   b) Habeas corpus: _____

   _____

   c) The Bill of Rights: _____

   _____

   d) Parliamentary monarchy: _____

   _____

3. Name two rights that were proclaimed in the 1689 Bill of Rights.

   • _____

   • _____

④ Each of the three following figures had opinions about which political system was best.
Write down the name of each person and fill in the details on these index cards.

Country: _____

Year of birth: _____

Year of death: _____

Best political system, in his opinion: _____
_____
_____
_____

Country: _____

Year of birth: _____

Year of death: _____

Best political system, in his opinion: _____
_____
_____
_____

Country: _____

Year of birth: _____

Year of death: _____

Best political system, in his opinion: _____
_____
_____
_____

5 Define the French Revolution in your own words.

_____

_____

6 Find one similarity and one difference between the English Revolution of 1689 and the French Revolution of 1789.

a) Similarity: _____

_____

_____

_____

b) Difference: _____

_____

_____

_____

7 Complete the table below showing the changes brought by the French Revolution.

	Before the French Revolution	After the French Revolution
Political system	_____	_____
Constitution	◯ Yes ◯ No	◯ Yes ◯ No
Social hierarchy	_____	All citizens were equal.
Religion	Only the Roman Catholic faith was permitted.	_____

8 Several important events occurred during the French Revolution. Write down the significance of each of the following events.

a) The storming of the Bastille: _____

_____

b) The abolition of seigneurial rights: _____

_____

c) The Declaration of the Rights of Man and of the Citizen: _____

_____

9 The Declaration of the Rights of Man and of the Citizen was partly inspired by the rights acquired in England in the 17th century and partly by Enlightenment ideas in the 18th century.

The following rights and freedoms were affirmed in the Declaration of the Rights of Man and of the Citizen. Indicate the origin of each by checking the right box.

Rights and freedoms	Rights recognized in England, 17th century	Enlightenment ideas, 18th century
Right to justice		
Freedom of speech		
Freedom of thought		
Freedom of expression		
Freedom of religion		
Freedom of the press		

10 a) Show which of these statements apply to subjects and which to citizens.

	Subjects	Citizens
The leader has absolute power over them.		
They cannot participate in public life.		
They are all equal.		
They can replace any leader who fails to represent their interests.		
They have obligations to a seigneur.		
They can be imprisoned without trial.		
They choose their own leaders.		

b) Do you think you are a subject, or a citizen? Explain your answer.

_____

_____

_____

_____

11 From what you have learned in this Inquiry, write down at least two things people can do to bring about a more democratic society.

- _____

_____

- _____

_____

SUMMARIZE WHAT YOU HAVE LEARNED

Using the following words, write a short text describing society under the Ancien Régime and the French Revolution.

> citizen • subject • political system • freedom • equality • Enlightenment • revolution •
> Declaration of the Rights of Man and of the Citizen • absolute monarchy • right

_____

_____

_____

_____

_____

_____

RETURN TO THE SECTION "ON THE TRAIL"

Return to pages 68 and 69 and reread your answers to the questions. Reassess them in the light of what you have learned since. Then try to answer the two questions you wrote down on page 69. If you cannot, try to figure out why.

Discuss and Take a Stand

Since the political revolutions of the 17th and 18th centuries, fundamental rights have been recognized in many countries. In Quebec, individual rights are guaranteed by the Quebec Charter of Human Rights and Freedoms. Quebec's Charter was inspired by the documents you have studied, written more than two centuries ago in France and England. Making sure fundamental rights are respected is not always easy, especially since some of them contradict others.

TC Your teacher will give you a worksheet including questions with illustrations as clues. Try to answer the questions using the visual clues. Then discuss your answers with your classmates.

GLORY TO GOD IN THE HIGHEST, ON EARTH PEACE. GOOD WILL TOWARD MEN.

LIBERTY AND UNION NOW AND FOR EVER

ONE AND INSEPARABLE

On the Trail

Most people in Western societies today work in the service sector: commerce, health care, administration, teaching, etc. These jobs do not require much physical strength. In the 19th century, a large segment of the population worked in manufacturing. The work was in factories, and it was very hard. Today most people have enough money to meet their basic needs. They can take time off for recreation, too, and go on vacation. But this has not always been the case.

Look at the illustrations on these two pages, and answer the questions.

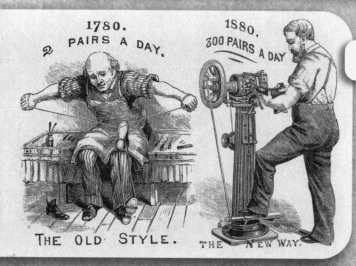

4.1 *Making shoes in 1780 and in 1880.*

4.2 *Car assembly plant, 2001.*

What difference do machines and robots make in manufacturing goods?

The machine still requires manual operation while the robot is programmed manually and automatically.

What new jobs have appeared since the age of electronics and computers?

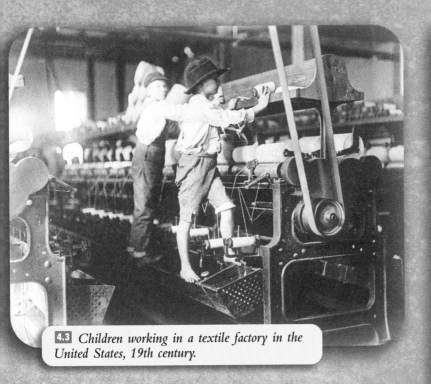

4.3 *Children working in a textile factory in the United States, 19th century.*

"In the cotton factories the ordinary hours of labor were from 6.30 a.m. till noon, and from 12.45 till 6.15 p.m. — this for five days in the week. On Saturday the mills close at noon. Sometimes the afternoon work is continued until 7.15 without stopping for supper, and less frequently the machinery is in continuous operation from 12.45 till 9 p.m., making eight and a quarter hours of uninterrupted work."

Report of the Royal Commission on the Relations of Capital and Labor in Canada, edited by James Armstrong and A.T. Freed. Ottawa: Queen's Printer, 1889.

4.4 *Companies today are concerned about the safety of their workers.*

Looking at these illustrations, describe how work conditions have improved since the 19th century.

_____

_____

_____

_____

_____

Write down two questions that come to mind about how the workplace has changed.

• _____

_____

_____

• _____

_____

_____

At a Glance

In What Context Did the Industrial Revolution Begin?

Until the 19th century, there was little change in the way goods were made. Manufacturing was mostly done by hand by artisans, and quantities were small. The situation changed in the 19th century. Manufacturing was increasingly done by machines, in factories, and larger quantities were produced. These were the beginnings of industrialization. The process began in England in the late 18th century, and in the 19th century spread to northern Europe and the United States.

4.5 INDUSTRIALIZED EUROPE IN THE LATE 19TH CENTURY

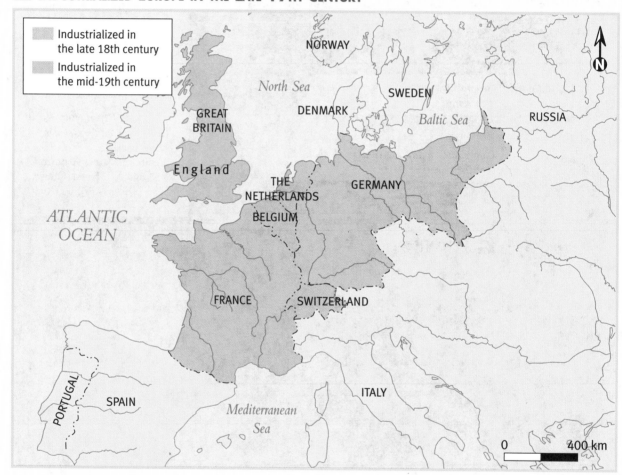

Legend:
- Industrialized in the late 18th century
- Industrialized in the mid-19th century

Advances in agriculture

In England, new agricultural techniques appeared and came into general use in the 18th century, such as
- crop rotation;
- use of animal manure as fertilizer;
- selection of higher-quality seed;
- improvement of the plough;
- invention of the thresher driven by a water wheel.

All these improvements resulted in increased agricultural yields. More food was produced than before, but by fewer workers. Farm hands who were put out of work would later be employed in the factories.

---

manufacturing: transforming raw materials into finished products, usually with machines.

industrialization: development of manufacturing on a large scale.

yield: the size of the harvest in relation to the surface cultivated.

CROP ROTATION

Ever since the Middle Ages, peasants in Europe had left part of their land fallow (uncultivated) every year so as not to exhaust the soil.

In the 18th century, the English discovered that they could cultivate all their fields if they rotated their crops. For example, legumes capture nitrogen, a gas present in the air, and fix it in the soil. Nitrogen is a natural fertilizer, so legumes enrich the soil. Grains, on the other hand, deplete the soil. Rotating these crops meant that land could keep its fertility while producing more.

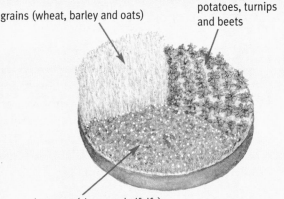

grains (wheat, barley and oats)

potatoes, turnips and beets

legumes (clover and alfalfa)

Population growth

From the late 18th century on, the population of Europe grew steadily. This growth was due to falling death rates, which in turn were due to improved nutrition and advances in public health. The population of Europe tripled between 1750 and 1900, the period that coincides with industrialization. Population growth was more pronounced in Great Britain than anywhere else in Europe.

Population growth in Europe led to increased demand for consumer goods.

Transportation

By the late 18th century, Great Britain had an impressive transportation network.

It had an excellent merchant navy. Ships brought raw materials from British colonies to British factories and then shipped manufactured goods to consumers all over Europe.

Great Britain also had a vast canal network for inland navigation. Raw materials and merchandise were moved back and forth across the country by canal in boats called barges.

However, transport was no faster than it had been in antiquity, as the power sources (wind, animal and human strength) were still the same.

4.6 *A canal in Great Britain.*

Mechanization of textile production

The English had been raising sheep for centuries and, up to the 18th century, artisans had been spinning and weaving woollen textiles.

As the 18th century progressed, more and more European consumers chose to buy coloured cotton cloth imported from India instead of English woollens. England gradually abandoned the production of woollen cloth and began to produce cotton, which it exported all over Europe. England purchased the raw material in its Australian, American and West Indian colonies, where prices were low because cotton plantations were run on slave labour.

---

canal: an artificial waterway created for navigation.

spin: to draw out and twist wool or cotton fibres to make thread for weaving.

weave: to cross threads over one another to make fabric.

textiles: synonym for cloth; the cloth manufacturing industry.

Cotton was in such high demand that inventors searched for ways to speed up the spinning and weaving process and to increase production.

The first inventions were aimed at improving weaving. Then inventors tried to accelerate spinning, too, to meet the rising demand for thread. The traditional spinning wheel was no longer good enough. After a few tries, one inventor perfected a machine called a spinning mule, which was much faster. The spinning mule was the first step in the mechanization of the textile industry.

By the end of the 18th century, English textile production was completely mechanized. This was largely thanks to the steam engine, another innovation of the era.

4.7 *Spinning wheel. The spinning wheel could only fill one spool at a time.*

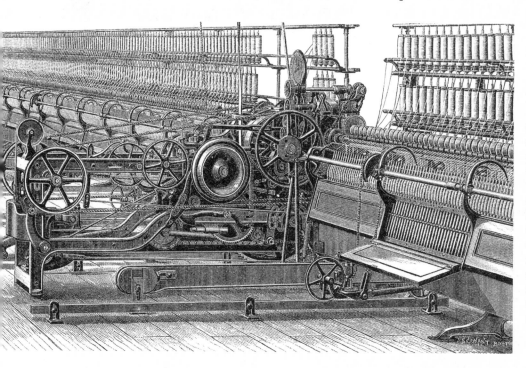

4.8 *Spinning mule. This machine could fill up to 30 spools at a time.*

Invented in 1779 by British weaver Samuel Crompton, the spinning mule was powered by a water wheel, and produced stronger thread than the spinning wheel. In the 19th century it was copied by cotton manufacturers throughout Europe and the United States. By replacing the work of several spinners, the spinning mule threw many artisans out of work.

4.9 INDUSTRIALIZATION

1783: Jouffroy d'Abbans's steamship

Circa 1780: Industrialization begins in England

Circa 1830: Industrialization begins in France

Circa 1840: Industrialization begins in the United States

1779: Samuel Crompton's spinning mule

1814: George Stephenson's steam locomotive

Circa 1850: Industrialization begins in Germany

1776: James Watt's steam engine

Circa 1890: Industrialization begins in Canada

MODERN TIMES	MODERN TIMES	MODERN TIMES	CONTEMPORARY ERA	CONTEMPORARY ERA	CONTEMPORARY ERA	CONTEMPORARY ERA	CONTEMPORARY ERA
1750	1775	1800	1825	1850	1875	1900	

Let's Get to Work!

1 What is the main activity of rural populations? Check the right answer.

○ The textile industry

○ Agriculture

○ Trade

2 a) Cotton was the raw material needed for the English textile industry in the 18th century. Where did England get it from?

_____

b) Why was this raw material so cheap?

_____

c) When was England first able to import this raw material? Go back to what you learned in Inquiry 2.

_____

_____

3 Compare a spinning mule to a traditional spinning wheel by completing the following table.

	Spinning wheel	Spinning mule
Quantity of thread produced		
Power source		
Mode of production: by hand or industrial?		

4 Artisans broke or set fire to many spinning mules. Why do you think they did this?

_____

_____

5 Look at the timeline (figure 4.9) on page 108.

a) What historical era ended with industrialization?

_____

b) What historical era began with industrialization? _____

6 a) What was the principal method of transporting merchandise in Britain in the late 18th century?

_____

b) What regions do you think were inaccessible using this method of transportation?

_____

7 Complete the diagram below.

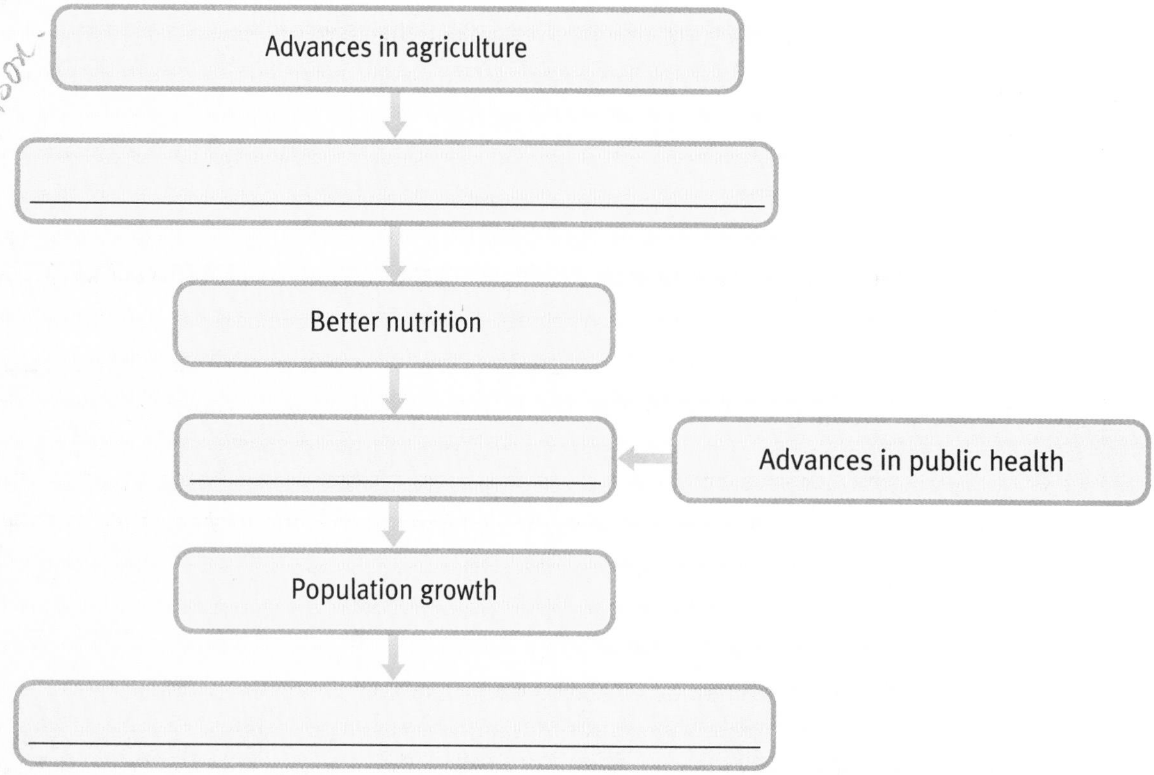

```
┌─────────────────────────────────────────────┐
│           Advances in agriculture             │
└─────────────────────────────────────────────┘
                     ↓
┌─────────────────────────────────────────────┐
│  _____  │
└─────────────────────────────────────────────┘
                     ↓
          ┌──────────────────────┐
          │   Better nutrition    │
          └──────────────────────┘
                     ↓
     ┌──────────────────────┐      ┌──────────────────────────┐
     │  _____   │ ←─── │  Advances in public health │
     └──────────────────────┘      └──────────────────────────┘
                     ↓
          ┌──────────────────────┐
          │   Population growth    │
          └──────────────────────┘
                     ↓
┌─────────────────────────────────────────────┐
│  _____  │
└─────────────────────────────────────────────┘
```

8 Cotton manufacturing required several steps. Compete the list.

1. Cotton harvested from plantations

2. Cotton transported by ship to Great Britain

3. _____

4. _____

5. Manufacturing clothing

9 Using the following terms, explain in your own words the difference between production by hand and industrial production.

┌──┐
│   speed • quantity • machine • power   │
└──┘

_____

_____

_____

_____

_____

_____

Project

Industrialization led to the economic and social development of Western countries. Industry has brought wealth to these countries. Today, however, many countries have hardly any industries, while others, known as emerging countries, are in the process of rapid industrial expansion. The standard of living in established industrialized countries, such as Canada and Great Britain, is very different from that in emerging countries.

Task: In this Inquiry, we invite you to study the differences between industrialized and emerging countries in the world today.

Final product required: A comparative table showing the similarities and differences among three countries: Great Britain (which was the first country to industrialize), Canada, and an emerging country.

Several steps are necessary to complete the project. Use the Project Planning Guide that your teacher will give you.

1 Choose an emerging country, in other words one that is in the process of industrialization. It could be Mexico, Brazil, China, India, South Africa, Argentina, Thailand, Indonesia, Colombia or another emerging country.

2 Collect information on the following aspects of your three countries:
- Economic wealth:
  – per capita income (GDP/population);
  – value of annual imports and exports;
  – percentage of country's wealth (GDP) spent on research and development (R&D).
- Employment:
  – unemployment rate;
  – percentages of GDP provided by agriculture, manufacturing and services.
- Urbanization:
  – rural and urban population percentages.
- Social development:
  – post-secondary education, or percentage of population educated beyond high school;
  – life expectancy.

3 Use this information to create a table.

4 Try to explain the differences and similarities found in your table.

How Did Industrialization Change the Economy of Great Britain?

In the late 18th century, industrialization in Great Britain accelerated. This was due to coal mining and iron processing. Industrialization changed Britain beyond all recognition. The change was so dramatic that the era is known as "The Industrial Revolution."

The steam engine

In 1776, British engineer James Watt invented a new machine that was to speed up industrialization: the steam engine.

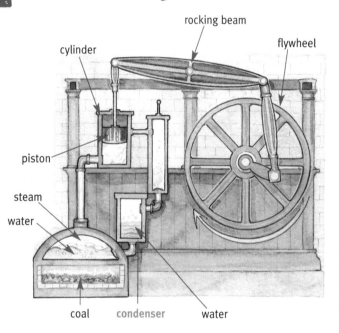

coal + water = steam ⟶ motion

4.10 *James Watt's steam engine.*

Using a coal fire, water was heated to produce steam. The steam rose into the cylinder and pushed the piston up, which moved the rocking beam so that the flywheel started turning. The motion of the flywheel drove a machine. The steam engine could thus be used as a motor to run a variety of machines. Its power was stronger and steadier than water power, wind power, animal power or human power.

---

condenser: a chamber in which steam is reduced to water through cooling.

ironmonger: metal merchant.

loom: a weaving machine.

THE EVOLUTION OF THE STEAM ENGINE

French inventor Denis Papin (1647 to 1714) was probably the first person to realize the potential of steam. He spent his life trying to build steam-driven machines, but never managed to make them work.

The first true steam engine was made in 1712 by an English ironmonger, Thomas Newcomen. It was used to pump water out of a coal mine. It was very slow, however, and often stopped altogether.

Steam was injected into the cylinder, followed by cold water to condense the steam. The water was then reheated to make more steam, and so on. This process consumed vast quantities of coal.

British engineer James Watt (1736 to 1819) was asked to repair a smaller version of Newcomen's steam engine in 1764. Over the next 25 years he made numerous improvements.

For example, he had the idea of condensing the steam in a separate condenser rather than in the cylinder itself. This consumed one fifth as much coal. Watt's steam engine was also much more powerful than Newcomen's model.

By 1800, there were nearly 500 steam engines in operation in Great Britain. James Watt invented numerous other industrial machines. The unit of power, the watt, is named after him.

Uses of the steam engine

- To pump water out of coal mines, which enabled miners to dig deeper
- To run steam hammers in iron foundries (see page 114)
- To run **looms** and spinning machines in textile factories
- To drive locomotives

Coal

Increasing use of steam engines led to an increase in the production of coal. Great Britain possessed several coal deposits (find them on map 4.12). Deep holes were bored into the ground and workers were sent down to dig out the coal. This is known as coal mining.

Coal became indispensable to industry, which is why the Industrial Revolution first occurred in areas of Great Britain that were rich in mineral deposits.

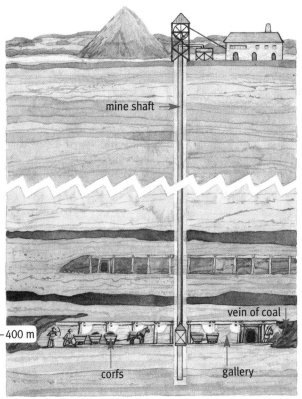

4.11 *Cross section of a coal mine.*

Uses of coal

- Running steam engines
- Heating houses
- Melting iron in iron foundries (see page 114)

---

ore: rock containing valuable metal.

charcoal: a fuel made of wood that has been burned in the absence of air.

smelt: to melt ore in order to extract the metal.

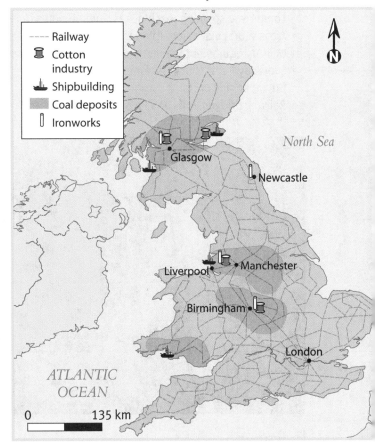

Iron processing

Great Britain had few iron deposits. In the 19th century it imported iron **ore** from Sweden and Russia.

Until 1830, **charcoal** was used for **smelting** iron ore. With charcoal, however, the iron ore could not be heated to a very high temperature. The resulting iron was of poor quality.

Coal began to replace charcoal in about 1830. Coal could be distilled to make coke, which could heat iron ore to a much higher temperature. Cast iron produced with coke was of higher quality. This was the birth of the steel industry.

In the mid-19th century, British engineer Henry Bessemer invented a method of making steel. Steel is made by adding a little carbon from coal to iron ore. Steel, which is very hard, gradually replaced iron.

- Looms and spinning machines (spinning mules, for example)
- Agricultural machinery (ploughs, for example)
- Military equipment (cannons and cannonballs, for example)
- Everyday items (buckets, for example)
- Steam engine parts
- Railway bridges, rails and locomotives

4.13 *James Nasmyth's foundry with steam hammer.*

In about 1830, a British mechanic named James Nasmyth set up a remarkable iron foundry near Manchester, which he fitted out with the best machine tools. He invented many of these tools himself, including the steam hammer.

The steam hammer was used to hammer huge blocks of cast iron into the desired shape. It was driven by a steam engine.

Railways

Until the early 19th century, in Great Britain, raw materials and manufactured goods were mostly transported along canals. Barges were towed by horses walking along the banks.

In 1814, British engineer George Stephenson had the idea of putting a steam engine on a car that could run along rails. The locomotive came into being. In 1825, his locomotive successfully hauled 20 passenger cars and 10 cars of coal.

Trains gradually replaced barges as a means of transport. They were faster, they could haul heavier loads and cost one sixth as much.

In 1830, Robert Stephenson, son of George, built the first passenger railway. It ran between Manchester and Liverpool and had a fixed time-table. Trains travelled at an average speed of 25 kilometres per hour.

Thousands of kilometres of railway were built throughout Great Britain. Look at the railway network on map 4.12, page 113.

4.14 *George Stephenson's locomotive.*

> What speed do you think trains travel at today?

Research Mandate

After the locomotive, other methods of transport were invented such as the streetcar, the subway and the automobile. Do some research on one of these methods to find out who invented it and how it works.

Let's Get to Work!

1 a) Coal, iron, steam engines and railways were the four pillars of industrialization. Show their interdependence by writing on the arrows what each one contributed to the other three.

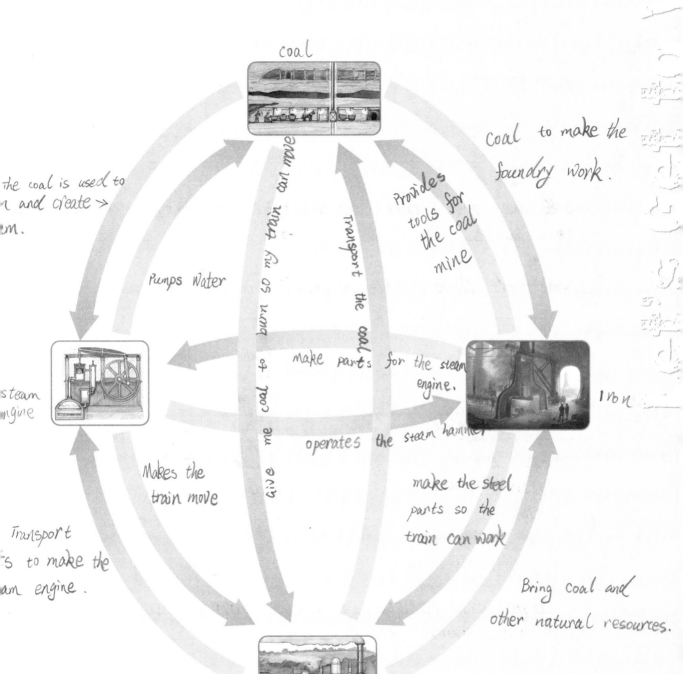

coal

the coal is used to ⟶ and create ⟶ em.

coal to make the foundry work.

Provides tools for the coal mine

Pumps Water

Transport the coal to burn so my train can move

make parts for the steam engine.

operates the steam hammer

Iron

steam engine

Makes the train move

give me coal

make the steel parts so the train can work

Transport s to make the an engine.

Bring coal and other natural resources.

Train

b) Which one of these four was used in the mining, processing and transporting of natural resources?

The steam Engine

2 Explain in your own words how a steam engine works.

It's a machine that works with heating water using coal. The steam creates pressure and makes the machine move.

3 Steam engines were not invented all at once. Explain the contribution of each of the following inventors.

Denis Papin:

Thomas Newcomen:

Built the first true steam engine for pumping water out of coal mines.

James Watt:

Improved Thomas Newcomen's steam engine.

4 In the table below, write down the sources of power that were used before the Industrial Revolution, and those that appeared during the Industrial Revolution.

SOURCES OF ENERGY	
Before the Industrial Revolution	**During the Industrial Revolution**
Man power	Steam Engine
Water, wind	Coal
animal	

5 a) From what you have learned up to now, name as many occupations as possible from the era of the Industrial Revolution.

Train conductor, coal miner, in iron monger, factory workers, spinners, weavers, farmers.

b) Circle the one that would have appealed to you the most.

c) Explain why you chose this occupation. _____

6 Use the following definitions to complete the crossword below.

1. Activity that precedes weaving in the cotton industry
2. Factory where iron is smelted for processing
3. The movable part that activates the rocking beam in a steam engine
4. He improved the steam engine
5. A stronger form of iron
6. Used as fuel in steam engines
7. Where the Industrial Revolution began
8. Method of transport invented during industrialization
9. Cloth industry

1. Spinning
2. Foundry
3. Piston
4. Watt
5. Steel
6. Coal
7. England
8. Railway
9. Textile.

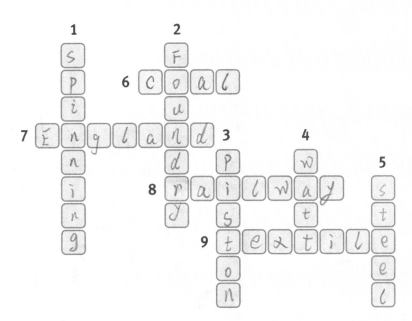

7 Complete the sentences below using the following words:

invention • steam engines • power • deposits • iron • steam

a) Industrialization first occurred in regions with many coal ___deposits___,
   as coal was needed to smelt the ___iron___ ore and to run the
   ___Steam engines___.

b) Industrialization was characterized by the ___invention___ and development
   of new technologies as well as by the use of new sources of ___power___,
   such as ___steam___.

New means of production

The Industrial Revolution was characterized by the
– **mechanization** of production
– concentration of production in factories.

The factory replaced artisans' own cottages as the place where production took place. Factories had many advantages:
– All the means of production, including buildings, machines, raw materials and workers, were in one location;
– With machines and a large workforce, goods could be produced in very large quantities and very quickly; production costs were therefore lower than if the goods were made by hand.

Goods made in factories were sold overseas as well as at home in retail stores. This was the start of mass consumption.

MEANS OF PRODUCTION		
	By hand	**Industrial**
Place of production	• Cottages	• Factory
Labour	• Artisans	• Factory workers
Tools used	• Manual tools	• Machines
Skills needed	• Specialized	• Unspecialized
Speed of production	• Slow	• Fast
Quantity produced	• Small	• Large
Cost of production	• High	• Low
Market	• Local	• Local and foreign

Would you say you live in a capitalist society? Why?

---

mechanization: the introduction of machinery into the production process.

entrepreneur: someone who starts or organizes a business or a factory.

capital: money needed to finance and operate a business.

Capitalism

Entrepreneurs did not usually have enough personal wealth to buy the means of production they needed. They began to finance their businesses in two ways:
– credit, or money borrowed from the bank; the bank stored people's savings and lent some of it to entrepreneurs, who paid it back with interest;
– they divided the capital into small amounts called shares; the people who bought them, the shareholders, would then share in the company's profits.

❊ **4.15** *The London stock exchange in the 19th century.* The stock exchange is the place where shares are bought and sold.

The economic system of investing capital in companies for the sake of profit is called capitalism.

Although it began in the 15th and 16th centuries with the growth of overseas trade, capitalism hit its stride during the Industrial Revolution.

Some investors became very rich. Their wealth gave them influence over politicians. These investors evolved into a new social class: the industrial bourgeoisie.

Let's Get to Work!

1 When we speak of industrialization in the 18th and 19th centuries, we use the word "revolution."

a) What is a revolution? You may use a dictionary.

A revolution is a change in how things are done.

b) In what way was industrialization a revolution? Explain.

How things were made

c) What type of revolution was it? Check the right answer.

○ Political revolution ○ Philosophical revolution

○ Artistic revolution ◉ Economic revolution

2 Using the following words, fill in the diagram below to show how capitalism worked.

workers • shareholders • capital • factory • wages • profit • labour

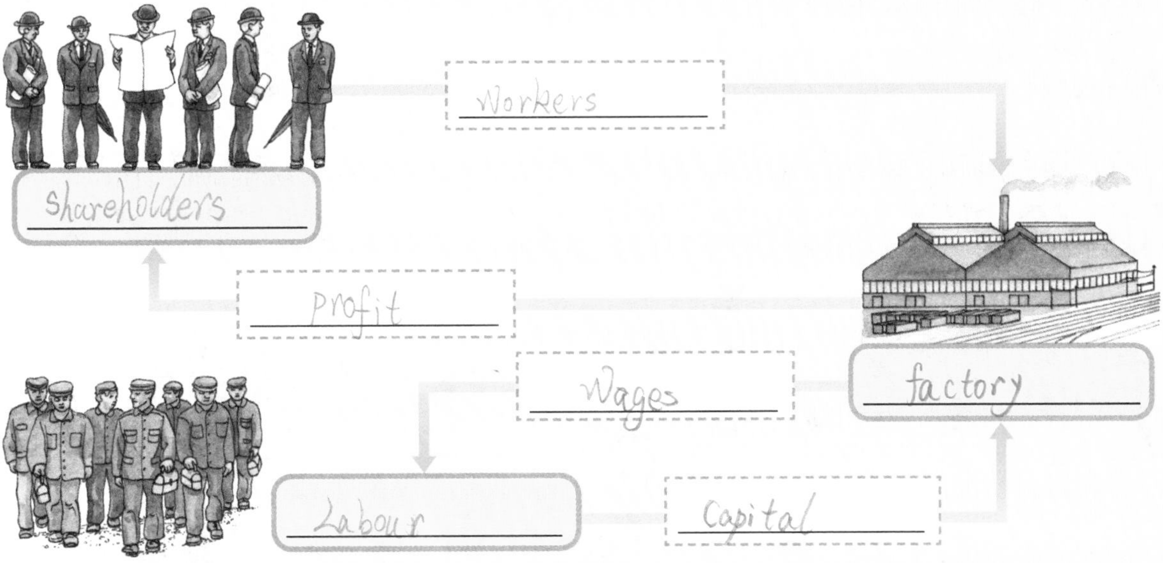

Workers

Shareholders

Profit

Wages

factory

Labour

Capital

3 a) When an investor deposits money in the bank, who pays interest to whom?

○ The bank pays interest to the investor. ○ The investor pays interest to the bank.

b) When the bank lends money to a borrower, who pays interest to whom?

○ The bank pays interest to the borrower. ○ The borrower pays interest to the bank.

4 How do you think businesses make a profit?

To sell something for more than what it costs

Inquiry 4 Industrialization: An Economic and Social Revolution **119**

How Did Industrialization Change British Society?

With industrialization, more people began to live in towns. New social classes came into existence. While industrialization benefited the bourgeoisie, the same was not true for the working class.

Urbanization

Technological advances in agriculture meant that fewer farm workers were needed. Many rural people left the countryside and moved to the city in the hope of finding work in the factories. This is known as the rural exodus.

Factories were built
– near coal mines;
– near railways or canals;
– in existing towns.

Towns in Great Britain grew rapidly in size and in number throughout the 19th century. Industrialization led to urbanization.

The districts where workers lived were built hastily and with no planning. They had no infrastructure. Lack of sanitation led to epidemics. With an increased demand for housing, rents went up. Workers lived in squalid conditions. Working-class districts were in striking contrast to bourgeois districts.

Working-class districts	Bourgeois districts
• Working-class districts were close to the factories. They were polluted by smoke.	• Bourgeois districts were far from the factories.
• Houses were small and crammed together. Epidemics such as cholera were frequent.	• They were spacious districts with plenty of green space. When illness struck, there was less risk of contagion.
• Because of the high rents, many families shared lodgings. They were badly heated, badly ventilated and humid.	• The industrial bourgeoisie lived in large comfortable houses and had servants.

4.16 *A British industrial town in the 19th century.*

urbanization: the process of people increasingly moving into towns.

MANCHESTER

Manchester was the first British town to industrialize (find it on map 4.12, page 113).

Manchester's first economic expansion took place in the Middle Ages with the manufacture of woollens. In the late 18th century, it moved into cotton production. Humid weather and the nearby coal deposits made it an ideal location for working with cotton.

Manchester's industries benefited from a large labour force recruited from the surrounding countryside. In 1830, a railway was built that linked Manchester to the port of Liverpool, where raw cotton was unloaded from ships.

French historian Alexis de Tocqueville visited Manchester in 1835.

"Look up and all around this place you will see the huge palaces of industry. You will hear the noise of furnaces, the whistle of steam. These vast structures keep air and light out of the human habitations which they dominate; they envelop them in perpetual fog; here is the slave, there is the master; there the wealth of some, here the poverty of most."

Alexis de Tocqueville,
Journeys to England and Ireland, 1835.
From *Alexis de Tocqueville on Democracy, Revolution, and Society*, edited by John Stone and Stephen Mennell.
University of Chicago Press, 1980.

Social classes

Industrialization brought a new social hierarchy to life in the towns. The three following social classes took shape.

Industrial bourgeoisie	Entrepreneurs, factory owners, bankers, merchants
Petty bourgeoisie	Lawyers, civil servants, journalists, doctors, engineers, skilled workers
Working class	Factory workers

The industrial bourgeoisie

In 19th-century Europe, the industrial bourgeois class began to dominate society. They lived comfortably and did not have to do manual work. They valued education, hard work and frugality.

The bourgeois class was the only one that benefited from Europe's economic growth in the 19th century.

The working class

Work conditions for the working class were extremely tough. They performed boring, repetitive tasks for 14 to 16 hours a day, six days out of seven. They were often supervised by very strict foremen. As workers were unskilled, they were easy to replace. If they got ill, or had an accident at work, or were too old, they were simply fired.

Work in the coal mines was particularly difficult and dangerous. Miners worked in suffocating heat, and fresh air was in short supply. A gallery could cave in at any moment. Miners often drowned in underground floods or were killed when firedamp exploded. Miners today still run the same risks.

A man's wages were not sufficient to support his family. His wife and children often had to work too, and worked for lower wages than the men for the same hours of work.

Miserable living conditions had drastic consequences: alcoholism, marital violence, prostitution, the abandonment of children. Because of the high infant death rate, life expectancy was 30 years or less. The only relief came from charities, which argued that the rich, according to their Christian values, should help the poor.

---

social class: group of people with the same economic position in society.

firedamp: a combustible gas present in coal mines.

CHILD LABOUR IN THE 19TH CENTURY

Children worked the same long hours as their fathers, but were paid a quarter of their wages.

They were hired in textile factories to repair broken threads because they were so small and agile that they could crawl under the looms while they were still running. They were also used for cleaning spools and gathering up thread.

Many children worked in mines. As some galleries were only 45 centimetres high, children were sent along them to extract the coal. They were also used for pushing corfs (wagons) of coal from the coal face to the bottom of the mineshaft.

It was not unusual to see child labourers as young as six years old. At the time, few people cared about the quality of life of these children, and many died young of exhaustion, illness or accidents. Those who survived were often permanently stunted as a result of such heavy work at such a young age.

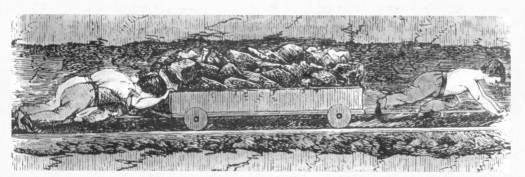

Children working in a coal mine in 19th-century England.

Have you read *Oliver Twist*, the novel by English author Charles Dickens? He tells the story of a young orphan in the era of industrialization. If you have read it, what can you remember about it?

Research Mandate

Is child labour permitted in Quebec? Is it permitted anywhere in the world? Why? Do some research to find out.

The quality of life for workers was very different from that for the owners, as the following table shows.

Life for the workers	Life for the owners
• They worked in factories or mines; their workplaces were unhealthy, dirty, badly ventilated and dangerous. Many workers were injured or killed by machinery.	• They usually worked in offices that were clean and safe.
• They had no time for recreation, as they often worked six days out of seven.	• They had time for recreation: they read newspapers, visited museums and libraries, travelled, dined in restaurants.
• A worker's wages were not enough to support a family; his wife and children had to work too.	• The wives and children of the bourgeoisie did not work.
• Children did not go to school.	• Children went to school and university.
• The family income was just enough to buy food. Working-class families could not afford to buy the goods they were manufacturing.	• They shopped in retail stores and bought the goods manufactured by the working class.

Let's Get to Work!

1 a) What do you think was the advantage of building a factory close to a coal mine?

To have easy access to the coal

b) What do you think was the advantage of building a factory close to a railway line?

To transport faster,

2 The three graphs below show urban and rural population percentages in England at various times in history.

a) Place the three graphs in chronological order by writing each of the following dates underneath the correct graph: 1800, 1850 and 1910.

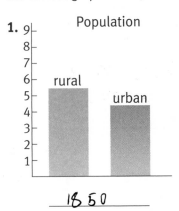

1850

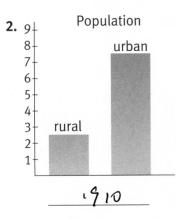

1910

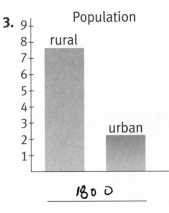

1800

b) What do we call the phenomenon that these graphs illustrate?

Rural exodus / Urbanization

3 In 1800, the population of Liverpool was 82,000. In 1850, it was 397,000.

a) Show this increase in population on the graph below.

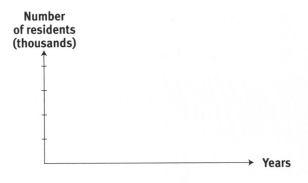

b) What do you observe from your graph?

The population of Liverpool went up

4 Use the following words to complete the table below comparing working-class and bourgeois districts.

> overcrowded housing • large houses • green space • near factories • comfort • lack of sanitation • cultural life • epidemics

Characteristics of working-class districts	Characteristics of bourgeois districts
Overcrowded housing	large houses
Near factories	green space
lack of sanitation	comfort
Epidemic	cultural life

5 a) Read the statements below and match each one to the individual who might have made it.

> an entrepreneur • a worker • an engineer • a child labourer

1. I give employment to many working-class families. _Entrepreneur_
2. I work in places that are hard to reach. _Child Labourer_
3. All day long I use pliers to handle hot iron. _A worker_
4. I invented the "rolling-mill," a cylinder that is used to roll out cast iron. _Engineer_
5. I work very hard and my wages are not enough for my family to survive on. _A worker_

b) Match the individuals in part a) with their appropriate social class.

1. Industrial bourgeoisie: _Entrepreneur_
2. Petty bourgeoisie: _Engineer_
3. Working class: _A worker / Child labourer._

6 a) Read this passage discussing child labour in Canada in the 19th century.

> "In some parts of the Dominion the employment of children of very tender years is still permitted. This injures the health, stunts the growth and prevents the proper education of such children, so that they cannot become healthy men and women or intelligent citizens."
>
> *Report of the Royal Commission on the Relations of Capital and Labor in Canada,* edited by James Armstrong and A.T. Freed. Ottawa: Queen's Printer, 1889.

b) Why do you think children's work was bad for their education?

If children are working all day long, then they won't have time or energy to devote to their education

7 Complete this table to compare workers with entrepreneurs.

	Workers	Entrepreneurs
Source of income	Salary	profits
Description of work	Labor intensive and repetitive	Working in a calm quiet clean office. Very relaxed.
Housing	Cramped, crowded, crowded and dirty	Large. clean, servants.
Children's activities	work	School, sports, museums.

8 a) Why do you think so many workers in the 19th century died before they reached the age of 40? Check the right answer or answers.

☑ They could not afford medical care.

☑ There were so many work accidents.

☑ They worked too hard.

☑ They caught epidemic diseases.

b) Is life expectancy the same for workers in Western societies today as it was in the 19th century? Why or why not?

No, because we work in more sanitary environments, we have labor laws that protect the workers.

9 a) If a worker in the 19th century survived into old age, what would become of him? Check the right answer.

☑ His boss would give him a pension.

◯ The government would give him a pension.

☑ He would be laid off and would have no more income.

b) What do you think the situation in Western countries is today?

Today when you reach 65/60 you get a pension from the government

10 If you had lived in the 19th century, what solution would you have proposed to the problem of child labour?

You would have taken pictures to show the would what is happening. Human Rights, strike.

Trade unions

In the mid-19th century, workers in Great Britain began to organize so they could demand better working conditions. They formed organizations called trade unions, and went on strike. The government banned strikes, however. It considered that strikes were an attack on the rights of entrepreneurs to make a profit.

4.17 *Miners' strike, 1893.*

The protests that accompanied strikes were often violently suppressed by the police and sometimes ended in a bloodbath.

Union demands in the 19th century

- Higher wages
- Reduced working hours
- Right to strike

 Can you name some of the demands trade unions are making today?

---

trade union: an association of workers with the aim of protecting their interests.

strike: workers refusing to work with the aim of achieving better working conditions.

proletariat: the class of workers who must sell their labour to survive.

Socialism

Trade unions found allies among some members of the petty bourgeoisie who were sympathetic to their plight. In Great Britain and other European countries, they founded socialist political parties. These parties put pressure on governments to pass laws that would improve working conditions for labourers.

Some radical socialists went further. They wanted to overthrow capitalist society and transfer power to the workers. One of these radical socialists was Karl Marx, a German philosopher and economist.

KARL MARX (1818 to 1883)

Karl Marx came from a bourgeois family. He studied history. He thought that history showed a perpetual struggle between social classes, in this case between the bourgeoisie and the proletariat. Marx saw the culmination of this struggle in the capitalist society of his time. He believed that the struggle would inevitably end in a violent revolution, and that the proletariat would emerge victorious. Marx called on the proletariat in all countries to unite and organize a revolution to overthrow capitalist society.

※ Marx explained his ideas in *The Communist Manifesto*, which he wrote in London in 1848 with his friend Friedrich Engels. In 1849, he moved to England for good.

Economic liberalism

The industrial bourgeoisie had a completely different way of seeing things. Unlike the socialists, they were against the government passing any laws that benefited workers. They insisted that entrepreneurs should be free to hire and fire whomever they chose, and to set workers' wages and work hours themselves. They believed that government intervention would reduce their profits and therefore harm the country's economy. This doctrine was known as "laissez-faire," or economic liberalism. It was an ideology that Scottish economist Adam Smith had first put forward in the 18th century.

ADAM SMITH (1723 to 1790)

In his work *An Inquiry into the Nature and Causes of the Wealth of Nations*, published in 1776, Scottish economist Adam Smith introduced the concept of "laissez-faire." The government should not interfere in the economy, he said. Its role should be to maintain order, build infrastructure (roads, bridges, drains, etc.), and administer justice, education and defence. Adam Smith was in favour of capitalism. He thought that by pursuing profits, entrepreneurs would bring prosperity to their country.

Adam Smith developed his ideas at the very start of the Industrial Revolution. He had no idea of the disastrous effects capitalism would have on working-class people.

Labour laws

In spite of opposition from liberals, the socialist party, backed by the trade unions, ended up persuading the British government to pass laws that improved the lives of the working class. Other industrialized countries in Europe followed suit.

Labour laws passed in Great Britain in the 19th century

1801: No employment of children under eight years old

1824–25: Authorization of some trade unions

1833: No employment of children under nine years old

1833: Workers under 18 years old must not work more than 80 hours a week, and workers under 13 years old, no more than 48 hours a week

1876: Introduction of compulsory elementary school

1878: No employment of children under ten years old

1891: Free education

1910: Minimum wage introduced

> If you didn't go to school, what would you do instead? Why is it compulsory to go to school?

Let's Get to Work!

1 What do you think an entrepreneur would have done if a worker had complained about working conditions?

He would have gotten fired.

2 What was the role of the trade unions? *To improve the lives of workers.*

3 a) Is a strike an individual or a group action? *Group.*

b) Think about the consequences of the strike for the entrepreneur. Why do you think trade unions chose this pressure tactic?

He would lose money because the workers be working.

4 Match each of the following statements with advocates of either socialism or economic liberalism.

	Advocates of socialism	Advocates of economic liberalism
We are in favour of capitalism.		✓
We want laws that will improve working conditions.	✓	
We are in favour of free enterprise.		✓
We want school to be compulsory.	✓	
We are members of the bourgeoisie.		✓
We support trade unions.	✓	

5 Use the following words to fill in the gaps in the statements below.

> Adam Smith • Karl Marx • socialists • liberalism • laws • ideologies • child • government • freedom to conduct business • revolution

a) In the era of industrialization, two __Ideologies__ were in conflict over the role that government should play in the economy.

b) __socialists__ believed that the government should intervene to pass __laws__ governing working conditions in the factories and about __child__ labour.

c) Some intellectuals, such as __Karl Marx__, even hoped for a __revolution__ that would overthrow capitalism.

d) __Liberalisam__, a doctrine advocated by __Adam Smith__, was against the __government__ interfering in the economy.

e) Supporters of this doctrine believed in protecting the __freedom to conduct busine__ so that entrepreneurs' profits would not decrease.

6 The law forbidding child labour and the law making education compulsory complemented each other. Explain this by answering the following questions.

a) How did the law forbidding child labour help ensure compliance with the law on compulsory education?

__If children have to attend school, they therefore have no time to work.__

b) How did the law making education compulsory help ensure compliance with the law forbidding child labour?

__If children can't work, then they have to go to school__

How Did the United States Become Industrialized?

The United States began to industrialize in the 1840s. Its population and economy grew rapidly. In the early 20th century, the United States became the leading industrial world power. Inventors were bursting with ideas, and ambitious entrepreneurs made vast fortunes. As in Great Britain, a labour movement arose to defend the rights of workers.

Population growth

Beginning in the mid–19th century, tens of thousands of unemployed Europeans arrived in America each year, full of hope that they could improve their lives. America welcomed a spirit of initiative, and some started up businesses that thrived. Many others, however, earned a poor living in the factories. Between 1870 and 1900, 15 million Europeans emigrated to the United States.

4.18 THE UNITED STATES IN THE LATE 19TH CENTURY

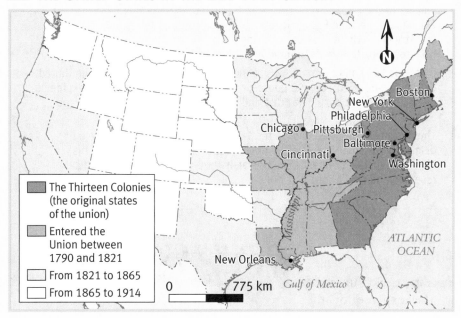

Legend:
- The Thirteen Colonies (the original states of the union)
- Entered the Union between 1790 and 1821
- From 1821 to 1865
- From 1865 to 1914

0 — 775 km

Inventions

1876: The telephone: Alexander Graham Bell

1877: The microphone: Emil Berliner

1879: The electric light bulb: Thomas Edison

1888: The roll of film: George Eastman

1893: The gasoline-powered automobile: the Duryea brothers

1903: The airplane: brothers Wilbur et Orville Wright

✳ THE STEAMSHIP

In the 19th century, the steamship gradually replaced the sailing ship. Steamships were invented in 1793 by French engineer Jouffroy d'Abbans. In 1807, an American engineer named Robert Fulton began to market them in the United States.

Steamships had a steam engine that drove two paddle wheels. Paddle steamers were only used for river transportation, as they used up too much coal to be viable for ocean crossings. In the 19th century, paddle steamers plied all the major American rivers, especially the Mississippi, which empties into the Gulf of Mexico.

paddle wheel

Paddle steamer.
How can you tell that these ships ran on steam power?

Ambitious entrepreneurs

Businessmen sometimes started from nothing and built companies that prospered. Some even became billionaires. Two such entrepreneurs were automobile manufacturer Henry Ford and oil magnate John Davison Rockefeller. The entrepreneurial spirit of these men helped raise the United States to the status of a great world industrial power.

✻ JOHN DAVISON ROCKEFELLER (1839 to 1937)

John D. Rockefeller was one of the first great capitalists. He was born in New York State, studied business and then worked for a few years as an accountant.

When the first oil wells were being drilled in Pennsylvania, Rockefeller devoted himself to the **refining** industry. In 1870, he founded the Standard Oil Company (which later became Esso). He gradually took control of the entire refining industry in the United States by buying out all his competitors. He did not shrink from resorting to threats, intimidation and corruption to achieve his goals.

By about 1880, his company was refining 90% of the petroleum in the United States. It employed 100,000 people, operated 22 oil wells and several pipelines. The company had become a **trust** and gained a **monopoly** over the United States oil industry.

The passing of antitrust laws in the 1890s, however, forced Rockefeller to dismantle his company. After he pulled out of the industry, he used his immense fortune to finance the University of Chicago as well as medical research and education.

The labour movement

As in Great Britain, the meteoric rise of American industry took place at the expense of the working class.

✻ Workers nationwide formed an association called the Order of the Knights of Labor. Founded in 1868, the Knights invited workers to local mixed assemblies, without regard to skill or sex. The only workers excluded from their meetings were lawyers, bankers and liquor manufacturers.

One of the goals of the Knights was better working conditions for workers. The Knights were very popular in spite of being repressed during strikes. By 1886 there were about 700,000 members. On May 1 of that year, there was a strike in Chicago. This date was later chosen as International Workers' Day. The Knights of Labor spread to Canada and to Quebec.

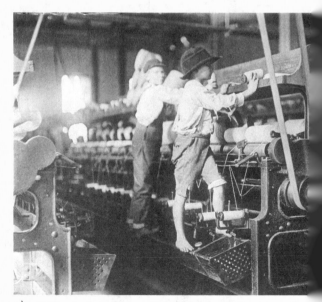

✻ **4.19** *Children working in a textile factory in the United States in the 19th century.*

---

refining: the process of purifying crude oil into petroleum products, such as gasoline.

trust: company which has a monopoly.

monopoly: absolute control of an economic sector, with no competitors.

Let's Get to Work!

1 a) Why did so many Europeans emigrate to the United States in the 19th century?

_____

b) Were their expectations realistic? Why?

_____

_____

_____

2 a) What social class do you think John D. Rockefeller belonged to by the end of the 19th century?

○ To the industrial bourgeoisie

○ To the petty bourgeoisie

○ To the working class

b) Do you think the majority of Americans belonged to this class?

_____

3 What means did Rockefeller use to increase the size of his company?

_____

_____

4 a) What was the Order of the Knights of Labor? Check the right answer.

○ A sports team

○ A trade union

○ An association for entrepreneurs

b) What did the Knights want?

_____

c) What was their main pressure tactic?

_____

d) Do you think the Knights believed in liberal or socialist ideas?
Explain your answer.

_____

_____

_____

_____

_____

M **5** This table shows the weekly budget for a working-class family of five in Philadelphia in 1851. Look at the budget and then answer the questions.

Weekly budget for a working-class family	
Food	$4.26
Heat and light	$0.54
Household maintenance	$0.25
Rent	$3.00
Linen	$0.20
Clothes	$2.00
Newspapers	$0.12
Total	$10.37

a) What was the family's main expense? Do you know why?

_____

b) What percentage of the budget does your answer to part a) represent? Show your calculations.

_____

c) What do you think would happen if the father of a family fell ill?

_____

_____

_____

6 Look at this painting showing European emigrants waiting for the ship that will take them to the United States.

a) Why do you think they are leaving Europe?

_____

_____

b) Which social class do you think they belong to?

◯ The bourgeoisie

◯ The petty bourgeoisie

◯ The working class

c) Based on what you have learned, what kind of life awaits them in the United States?

_____

_____

_____

✳ *Adolfo Tommasi*, The Emigrants, *1908.*

How Did Germany Become Industrialized?

Industrialization reached Germany in about 1850. Germany developed its industries using technological innovations such as oil drilling, electricity, chemistry and the internal combustion engine. Its main industrial region was the Ruhr Valley.

The Ruhr Valley

Industrialization in Germany was founded on the rich coal deposits that lay beneath the Ruhr Valley. It is still one of the most industrialized regions in the world. In the 19th century, it produced iron and steel, chemical products and textiles. Today it specializes in high-tech industries and renewable energy development.

4.20 *German working-class family in the early 20th century.*

Labour laws

Entrepreneur Alfred Krupp (1812 to 1887) set up a medical insurance program for his workers, as well as a pension plan for those who were too old to continue working.

Between 1883 and 1889, the German Chancellor (prime minister) Otto von Bismarck adopted a series of social insurance schemes inspired by the ones in Krupp's factories. Bismarck hoped these measures would prevent the growth of the socialist movement.

4.21 INDUSTRY IN 19TH-CENTURY GERMANY

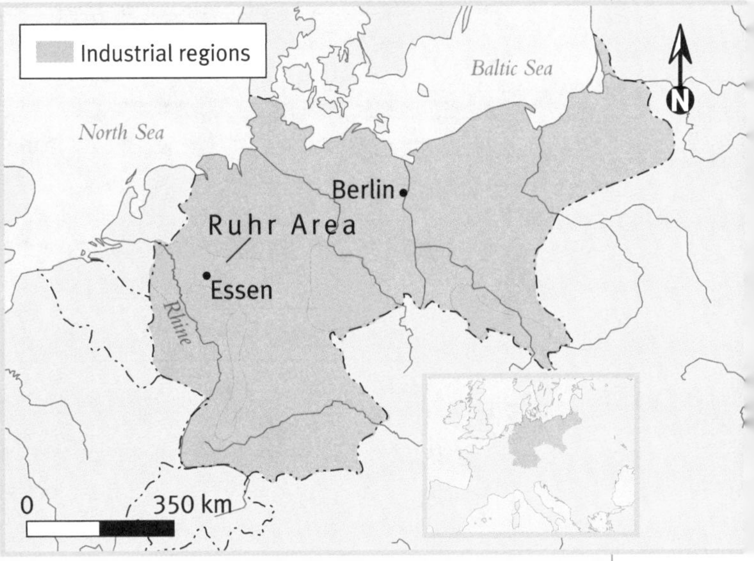

THE KRUPP COMPANY

The Krupps were a family of German industrialists who had settled in Essen, in the Ruhr Valley, in the 16th century. In 1812 Friedrich Krupp built a steel foundry. His son Alfred later built axles and wheels for trains, and then moved into making **armaments**. In 1847, he was the first to manufacture cannons out of steel. He owned mines as well as modern iron and steel plants. In 1902 the family acquired **shipyards**. By now it controlled a mighty industrial empire and was one of the leading families in Germany.

During the First World War (1914–18), the company made weapons for the powerful German army.

A Krupp factory in Essen.

armaments: weapons.

shipyard: a place where ships are built.

Let's Get to Work!

1 The industrialization of Germany was founded on what natural resource?

_____

2 The Krupp family owned coal mines, iron foundries, steel plants and shipyards. Each industry provided essential materials for another of the Krupp industries. Complete the diagram below, showing these links.

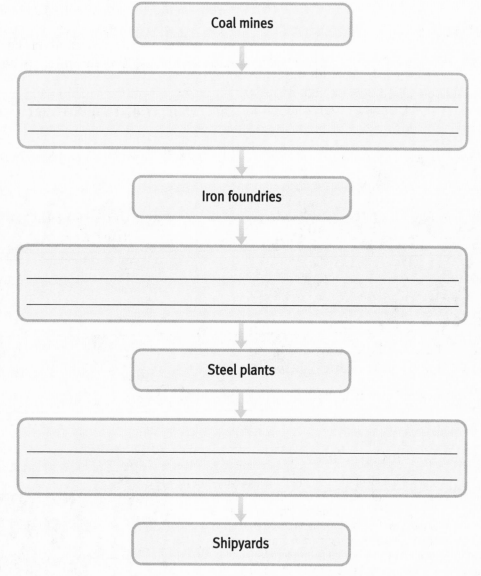

Coal mines

_____
_____

Iron foundries

_____
_____

Steel plants

_____
_____

Shipyards

3 a) German Chancellor Otto von Bismarck passed social legislation, even though he was opposed to socialism. Why?

_____

b) What British associations demanded similar labour laws?

_____

Synthesis Activities

1 In this Inquiry, find four inventions from the 18th and 19th centuries that contributed to industrializing the production of goods. Fill in the details on these index cards.

Name of invention: _____

Name of inventor: _____

Year it was invented: _____

Progress due to this invention:

_____

_____

Name of invention: _____

Name of inventor: _____

Year it was invented: _____

Progress due to this invention:

_____

_____

Name of invention: _____

Name of inventor: _____

Year it was invented: _____

Progress due to this invention:

_____

_____

Name of invention: _____

Name of inventor: _____

Year it was invented: _____

Progress due to this invention:

_____

_____

(2) Draw a diagram that explains industrialization.

(3) Read the two excerpts below. Underneath each one, write down whether the person who wrote it believed in economic liberalism or socialism.

a)

"We have observed that, as a general rule, the business of life is better performed when those who have an immediate interest in it are left to take their own course, uncontrolled either by the mandate of the law or by the meddling of any public functionary."

John Stuart Mill, *Principles of Political Economy*. Boston: Little & Brown, 1848.

_____

b)

"Masses of labourers, crowded into the factory, are organized like soldiers ... Not only are they slaves of the bourgeois class, and of the bourgeois State; they are daily and hourly enslaved by the machine, by the over-looker, and, above all, by the individual bourgeois manufacturer himself."

Karl Marx, *The Communist Manifesto*, 1848.
Edited by Jack Wayne. Toronto: Canadian Scholars' Press, 1987.

_____

4 Complete the diagram below showing various attempts to improve the lives of the working class in the 19th century.

ATTEMPTS TO IMPROVE THE LIVES OF THE WORKING CLASS

Trade unionism	Socialism	Labour laws
Definition: _____ _____ _____	Definition: _____ _____ _____	Definition: _____ _____ _____
Goal: _____ _____ _____ _____	Goal: _____ _____ _____ _____	Goal: _____ _____ _____ _____
Example of trade union: _____ _____ _____ _____	Example of socialist party: _____ _____ _____ _____	Examples of labour laws: _____ _____ _____ _____

5 Imagine you are an entrepreneur or else a worker.

a) Explain what you think about industrialization.

_____

_____

_____

_____

_____

_____

b) Have a debate with your classmates and defend your character's ideas.

Inquiry Conclusion

SUMMARIZE WHAT YOU HAVE LEARNED

Using the following words, write a short text to explain the effects of industrialization on society in England and on its economy.

> Industrial Revolution • means of production • capitalism • town • social class • bourgeoisie • worker • trade union • law

_____

_____

_____

_____

_____

_____

_____

RETURN TO THE SECTION "ON THE TRAIL"

Return to pages 104 and 105 and reread your answers to the questions. Reassess them in the light of what you have learned since. Then try to answer the two questions you wrote down on page 105. If you cannot, try to figure out why.

Discuss and Take a Stand

Industrialization took place in several phases. The first, which began in the 18th century, was characterized by the use of steam engines and coal. The second, at the turn of the 20th century, occurred because of two new energy sources: oil and electricity. Today we are experiencing a third industrial phase, characterized by the growth of the electronics industry and the use of a variety of energy sources, such as electricity and oil, but also solar, nuclear and wind power.

TC Your teacher will give you a worksheet including questions and illustrations as clues. Try to answer the questions using the visual clues. Then discuss your answers with your classmates.

On the Trail

When countries lack the raw material they need for manufacturing commodities, they acquire them through international trade. Afterwards they often sell the commodities a long way from where they were made. World trade does not benefit all countries equally. The most powerful countries exploit the raw materials that they find in other countries for profit, often to the detriment of the local people.

Look at the illustrations on these two pages and then answer the questions.

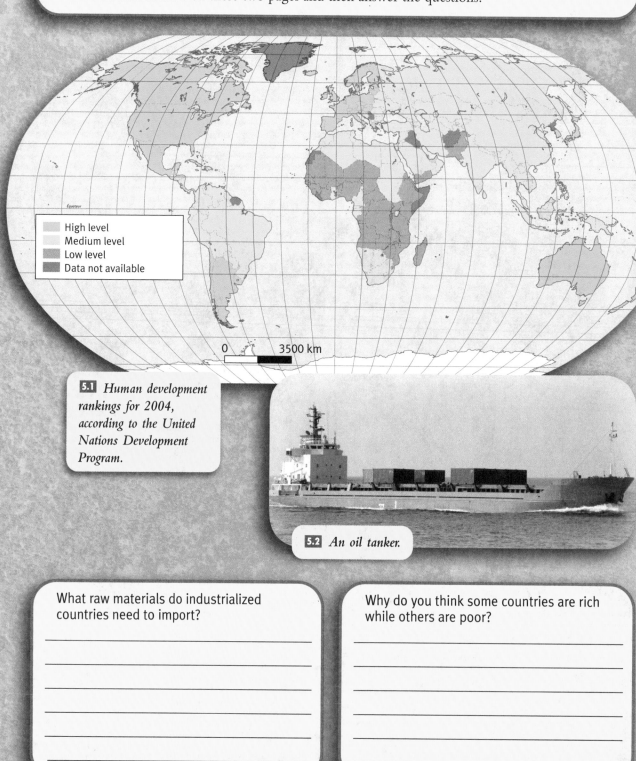

High level
Medium level
Low level
Data not available

0   3500 km

5.1 *Human development rankings for 2004, according to the United Nations Development Program.*

5.2 *An oil tanker.*

What raw materials do industrialized countries need to import?

_____

_____

_____

_____

_____

Why do you think some countries are rich while others are poor?

_____

_____

_____

_____

_____

Flag of the United Kingdom.

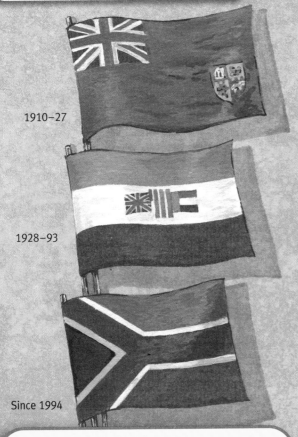

5.4 *Flags of South Africa since 1910, as a British colony and an independent country.*

1910–27

1928–93

Since 1994

5.5 *Africans submitting to European colonizers in the 19th century.*

What is the difference between an independent country and a colony?

_____

_____

_____

_____

_____

Write down two questions that come to mind about the effects of colonization.

• _____

_____

• _____

_____

_____

At a Glance

What Was the Context of the European Colonization of Africa?

In western European countries, industrialization contributed to economic expansion and population increase. One way to maintain this growth was to conquer more foreign lands and peoples.

The decline of colonization

Colonies founded by European states after the Age of Discovery began to demand their independence in the late 18th century. Look at map 2.21, on page 55, to remind you of which countries were colonized.

Nationalist movements

Revolutionaries in colonies throughout America began to launch wars and rebellions in the name of nationalism. Their mother countries were forced to grant them independence.

In 1783, for example, after a war that lasted six years, the United States of America gained independence from Britain.

In the early 19th century, rebellions in South America forced Portugal and Spain to grant independence to their American colonies, including Bolivia, Brazil, Colombia, Argentina, Chile and Peru. A majority of American colonies gained independence between 1816 and 1839.

Canada, however, was still a British colony at the time. It was only granted independence in 1867.

The abolition of slavery

The fate of African slaves in the plantations of America became a topic of concern, especially among human rights advocates and some European church groups, who saw slavery as contrary to Christian values.

These people began to put pressure on European states to halt the slave trade and abolish slavery, or slave labour, once and for all.

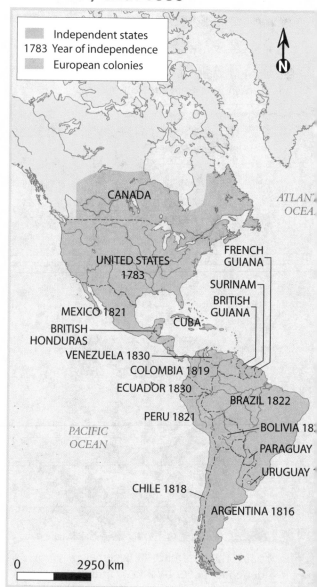

5.6 AMERICA, CIRCA 1860

Independent states
1783 Year of independence
European colonies

Country	Abolition of slave trade	Abolition of slavery
United Kingdom	1807	1833
France	1815–18	1848
United States	1808	1865

---

nationalism: a movement in which a people demands recognition as a full-fledged nation, capable of self-government.

5.7 *Proclamation of the abolition of slavery in the French colonies, April 23, 1848. François Auguste Biard, 1849.*

"Article 1. Slavery will be completely abolished in all the colonies and French possessions.

Article 8. In future, even in a foreign country, it is forbidden every Frenchman to possess, to buy or to sell slaves, and to participate, either directly, or indirectly, in any traffic or exploitation of this kind."

Excerpt from the Decree of the French Government Abolishing Slavery, April 27, 1848.

In 1850, colonization appeared to be coming to an end. One by one, plantation colonies (growing cotton, sugar and coffee) became independent countries. Europeans stopped buying or capturing human beings in Africa and forcing them to work in American colonies. The triangular trade was finally over (see Inquiry 2, page 55).

Reasons for the renewal of colonization

In the mid-19th century, however, Europe began to colonize new lands, this time in Africa, Asia and the South Sea Islands. Europe had several motives for embarking on these new conquests.

Economic motives

In 1850, nearly half of the world's manufacturing took place in Europe. Europe had the means of transportation to export its products.

However, it still needed
– raw materials for processing;
– markets where it could sell the commodities it made;
– new companies in which to invest its capital.

European economies depended heavily on raw materials that they could process into manufactured goods. The map below shows the raw materials imported by the United Kingdom (Great Britain and Ireland) in the 19th century.

5.8 **RAW MATERIAL IMPORTS TO THE UNITED KINGDOM, CIRCA 1850**

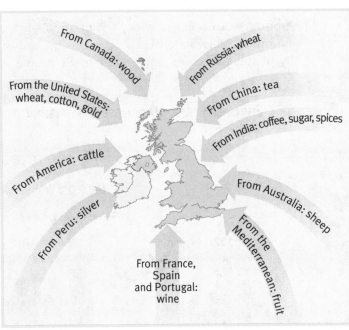

From Canada: wood
From Russia: wheat
From the United States: wheat, cotton, gold
From China: tea
From India: coffee, sugar, spices
From America: cattle
From Australia: sheep
From Peru: silver
From the Mediterranean: fruit
From France, Spain and Portugal: wine

invest: to put money into a company in order to make a profit.

5.9 *English immigrants in Australia reading the news from Europe.*

Political and social motives

In addition to economic motives, politics played a part too: European countries wanted to increase their human influence as well as expand their production capacity. Controlling other countries also gave them prestige.

From a social point of view, colonization offered Europe a chance to get rid of its excess population by obliging or encouraging the poorest people to go and live far away. Colonies of exploitation, which had existed solely to import raw materials, were soon outnumbered by colonies of settlement.

In the 19th century, around 50 million Europeans left the poorer regions of Europe to emigrate to the colonies. English emigrants went to Australia and Canada, for example, while thousands of French emigrated to Algeria after conflicts in France.

5.10 **EUROPEAN AND JAPANESE EXPANSION IN THE 19TH AND 20TH CENTURIES**

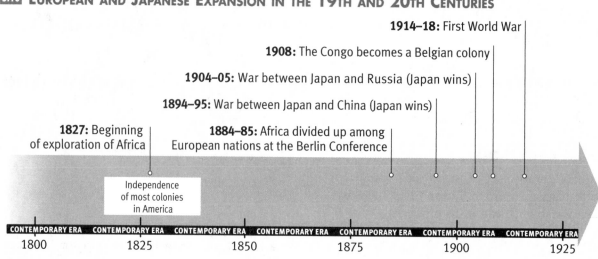

1914–18: First World War

1908: The Congo becomes a Belgian colony

1904–05: War between Japan and Russia (Japan wins)

1894–95: War between Japan and China (Japan wins)

1827: Beginning of exploration of Africa

1884–85: Africa divided up among European nations at the Berlin Conference

Independence of most colonies in America

CONTEMPORARY ERA	CONTEMPORARY ERA	CONTEMPORARY ERA	CONTEMPORARY ERA	CONTEMPORARY ERA	CONTEMPORARY ERA	CONTEMPORARY ERA
1800	1825	1850	1875	1900	1925	

Let's Get to Work!

1 Write down two reasons why colonization declined before 1850.

- slavery was abolished.
- The colonies wanted to be independent.

2 How do you think the abolition of slavery affected plantation owners?

The owners will have to start playing for workers and the profits will decrease.

3 Look at the table at the bottom of page 142. Compare the dates of the abolition of slavery in the United Kingdom, France and the United States.

a) Which country seems to have been most reluctant to abolish slavery?

USA

b) Why do you think this was?

The united states depended heavily on slaves so they didn't want to lose that.

4 Why do you think the inhabitants of the colonies wanted their independence? Suggest a few reasons.

They wanted their freedom to make decisions. to stop paying taxes to the mother country, to create their own government and legal system etc...

5 Name four European countries that had colonies on the American continent before 1850. For each country, name one of its former colonies.

Refer to what you learned in Inquiry 2 (map 2.21, page 55), a dictionary, or map 5.6, page 142.

European country	Colony in America
• Spain	Mexico, venezuela, Chile, Bolivia
• Portugal	Brazil
• France	Canada
• England	Canada, USA.

6 Use arrows to match each of the following statements with an economic need.

STATEMENT   ECONOMIC NEED

a) An entrepreneur wants
to invest capital in the building
of a railway, for profit.   1. Need for markets.

b) A shipbuilder needs wood
to build his ships.   2. Need for raw materials.

c) A clothing manufacturer needs
new customers for his products.   3. Need for investment opportunities for capital.

7 Why do you think industrialized countries had to seek raw materials elsewhere?

Europe didn't have the raw materials they needed. Also they didn't want to pay for them.

8 Match each of the following statements with either a colony of exploitation or a colony of settlement, or both.

	Colony of exploitation	Colony of settlement
Enabled Europe to get rid of excess population.		✓
Enabled exploitation of the colony's natural resources.	✓	
Had trade relations with the mother country.	✓	

9 a) Read the following passage from a speech by Jules Ferry, a 19th-century French politician who promoted the advantages of colonization for European countries.

> "The first form of colonization is that which offers asylum and work to the population overflow from poor countries, or from countries whose people are excessively fertile ... For rich countries, colonies are a most advantageous form of capital investment."
>
> Jules Ferry, *Journal officiel*, July 28, 1885. Free translation.

b) In the passage above, highlight
1. The phrase that illustrates economic motives for colonization in blue;
2. The phrase that illustrates social motives for colonization in yellow.

10 In your own words, explain why industrialization led to the need for colonies.

They needed the raw materials from the & colonies to make the products in Europe?

Project

The colonization of Africa has had many lasting effects on the peoples of the African continent. The issues facing Africa today are connected in one way or another to the colonial era. Each African country has a special relationship with its former mother country, whether in terms of immigration, trade, government structure, education, religion or humanitarian aid.

Task: In this Inquiry, we invite you to choose an African country (there are about 50) and collect some information on its history. Afterwards you will prepare a quiz for your class.

Final product required: A quiz with rules, a variety of questions and clear answers.

Several steps are necessary to complete the project. Use the Project Planning Guide that your teacher will give you.

 Choose an African country and collect some information on its colonial past by asking the following questions:
- Which European country colonized it?
- What were the important events in its history?
- When did it gain its independence?

 Find out about the country's characteristics today. Answer the following questions:
- What is the capital of the country?
- What languages are spoken?
- What languages are taught in school?
- What religions are practised?
- What other countries does it trade with?

 Invent some quiz questions about the country and its history using the information you collected. Don't forget to write out the answers. You can use multiple-choice questions, true-or-false questions or other kinds of questions, or think up other interesting activities.

 Add your questions to those of your classmates and create a quiz together. Write down the rules.

 Play the game.

How Did Europeans Colonize Africa? 欧 洲如何殖民非洲的？

Europeans knew very little about Africa in 1850. But by 1914, only half a century later, Europe had explored it and taken almost complete possession of it. Colonization was a bloody affair: Europeans took control of the African peoples by force. The main colonizers were the United Kingdom, France, Belgium and Germany.

The exploration of Africa 对非洲的去探索、

Africa possessed abundant natural resources:
– minerals (gold, diamonds, copper, etc.);
– ivory;
– rubber;
– wood.

The climate and the soil in Africa were excellent for growing coffee, cotton, sugar cane, peanuts, pepper and spices.

Europeans already controlled parts of the coast of Africa in the 19th century, and merchant ships stopped there for fresh supplies. Now, however, explorers began to penetrate the interior of this vast continent.

Why do people go on expeditions or safaris in Africa today? Do these activities benefit the people of Africa?

5.11 THE EXPLORERS OF AFRICA

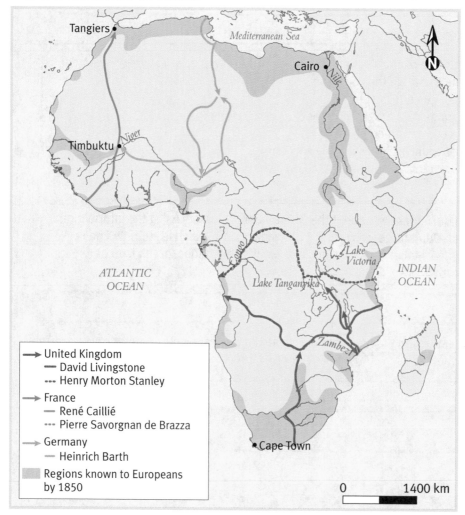

- → United Kingdom
  - — David Livingstone
  - --- Henry Morton Stanley
- → France
  - — René Caillié
  - --- Pierre Savorgnan de Brazza
- → Germany
  - — Heinrich Barth
- Regions known to Europeans by 1850

0 — 1400 km

In the 19th century, explorers were especially interested in the **hydrography** of Africa. They climbed to the source of the Nile and explored the Congo River as well as the interior Great Lakes.

Research Mandate

Do some research on other explorers of Africa, such as Richard Burton, John Speke, Samuel Baker and Florence Baker. What region of Africa did each of them explore?

hydrography: the science of mapping waterways.

✳ LEOPOLD II (1835 TO 1909)

Leopold II was King of Belgium from 1865 until his death in 1909. He and Henry Morton Stanley founded the International African Association, whose goal was to explore the African continent.

The king dreamed of a Belgian colony in Africa, and invested his personal fortune in exploration of the Congo. At the Berlin Conference of 1885, Congo was declared a "Free State," and came under the private ownership of Leopold II.

The king hoped to evangelize the inhabitants of the Congo. He also encouraged the production of rubber, ivory, hardwood and minerals, which were sent back to Belgium. During Leopold II's reign in the Congo, the inhabitants were treated brutally by the colonists, who subjected them to slavery (even though it was illegal), mutilation, malnutrition and mass murder.

Leopold II left the Congo to Belgium in his will. The Congo thus became a Belgian colony in 1908.

The exploration of Africa proceeded without the consent of Africans, who had no weapons to match the Europeans' arms, and so could not resist their entry.

The Berlin Conference

The explorations in Africa provoked conflict among European countries. When Henry Morton Stanley was exploring the Congo River basin, he clashed with Pierre Savorgnan de Brazza, who was exploring the same area for France. Portugal, too, was staking its claim in the region.

Other European countries hoped to have a share in Africa, too. Their race to take possession of it was known as the "scramble for Africa." In 1884, German Chancellor (prime minister) Otto von Bismarck organized the Berlin Conference. The aim of the conference was to settle the differences between the European countries competing for African colonies. The 15 countries represented at the conference agreed to let King Leopold II take the Congo. They also agreed that

- everyone must practise free trade in Africa (the freedom to do business without restriction);
- everyone could use the Congo and Niger rivers for shipping;
- slavery and the slave trade were prohibited;
- importing weapons into Africa was prohibited;
- to take possession of a region, a colonizing country must occupy it (establish a permanent presence there).

The Berlin Conference lasted from 1884 to 1885. By the time it ended, European colonizers had carved up the African continent among themselves, creating about 50 countries.

✳ HENRY MORTON STANLEY (1841 TO 1904)

Henry Morton Stanley was a British explorer who went to Africa for the first time as a journalist in search of another explorer, David Livingstone.

On his second trip, he crossed the African continent from east to west, exploring the Congo River.

In 1885, he founded the Congo Free State with King Leopold II.

Africans gave Stanley the nickname Boula-Matari, or "stone-breaker," because of his brutality towards the indigenous people.

Let's Get to Work!

1 What natural resources did Africa possess in the 19th century?

Minerals (Gold, diamonds, silver), ivory, rubber, wood.

2 Once he had taken possession of the Congo, how did King Leopold II take control in the political, economic and religious spheres?

a) Political sphere:

changed the rules of the country, charged taxes to belgium, enforce the laws, changed the school, changed the language, chang

b) Economic sphere:

All goods and natural resources were sent to Belgium for processing, and trading.

c) Religious sphere:

Changed the official religion to christianity and converted everyone.

3 Do you think the inhabitants of the Congo agreed with Leopold II becoming their ruler?

No, they had no say in the take over.

4 Why do you think European explorers used the rivers for travelling in Africa?

They used the rivers because it was the only means of transportation at the time.

5 The fifteen states that were present at the Berlin Conference decided to ban the importing of firearms into Africa. What do you think were the effects of this decision on Africans who wanted to resist colonization?

They banned the weapons so that the African people couldn't get a hold of them.

6 What regions of Africa did Europeans know about in 1850? Check the correct answer. See map 5.11 on page 148 for help.

○ Interior of the continent

☑ The Nile Valley, in Egypt

☑ The coastal regions

○ The great rivers: the Niger, Congo and Zambezi.

7 Why were European countries in conflict over Africa in the 19th century?

They all wanted the natural resources that Africa possessed.

8 From what you have learned so far, which three European countries seem to have led the "scramble for Africa"?

- *UK*
- *France*
- *Belgium and Germany*

9 What do you think would have happened if the countries at the Berlin Conference had broken the rules laid down there?

World war 1

10 Are the following statements true or false? If they are false, write the correct version underneath.

	TRUE	FALSE
a) The colonization of Africa was carried out peacefully.	○	✓
b) The African climate is not suitable for agriculture.	○	✓
c) King Leopold exploited the natural resources of the Congo for his own profit.	✓	○
d) Slavery was forbidden in Africa.	✓	○

11 Fill out the crossword below using the definitions given.

1. Country whose king was Leopold II.
2. City where the conference at which Africa was carved up was held.
3. Explorer who worked for France.
4. Right to do business without restriction (4, 5).
5. Stanley's nickname.
6. River used as a highway by explorers.

```
        1                    2
        B                    B                         3
4   F r e e t r a d e        e                         B
        l                    r                         r
        g            5   B o u l a - M a t a r i
        i                    i                         z
        u            6   C o n g o                     z
        m                                              a
```

European imperialism in Africa

When a state attempts to extend its rule over other countries, it is practising a policy known as imperialism. European countries' exploitation of African colonies was a form of imperialism.

Racial discrimination

Europe's technological, commercial and military superiority made Europeans feel they were superior to other peoples in every other sphere too: religion, culture, social organization and politics.

Europeans justified colonialism by seeing it as their mission to bring Europe's "superior" civilization to the "inferior" peoples of Africa and Asia. This excerpt from an 1885 speech by Jules Ferry, a member of the French government, is a good illustration of this way of thinking:

> "Gentlemen, we must speak more loudly and more honestly! We must say openly that the superior races have a right over the inferior races ... and this is because they have a duty. They have a duty to civilize the inferior races."
>
> Jules Ferry, Speech to the French Chamber of Deputies, March 28, 1885. Free translation.

The idea of European superiority over other peoples led to discrimination against them.

The idea of superiority was promoted widely through newspapers and school textbooks of the time. Most Europeans consequently came to accept it as true, and lent African colonization their support. Here, for example, is the definition of the word "Negro" in a 19th-century Larousse dictionary.

> ✴ "A few philanthropists have tried in vain to prove that the Negro race is as intelligent as the White race ... An indisputable fact, to be considered above all else, is that the Negro has a narrower, lighter and smaller brain than the White man ... Because he is endowed with the power of speech, we can enter into intellectual and moral relations with him, and attempt to raise him to our level, and we may succeed to a limited extent ... His intellectual inferiority, however, far from giving us the liberty to exploit his weakness, imposes on us the duty to help and protect him."
>
> Pierre Larousse, *Grand dictionnaire universel du 19e siècle* (Great Universal Dictionary of the 19th Century), 1873. Free translation.

5.12 *Catholic missionary in Africa.* The mission of educating the "inferior races" often took the form of evangelizing. Missionaries spread throughout Africa teaching Africans about the Christian religion. They were often accompanied by soldiers, who took control of the territories by force.

---

civilize: raise a primitive society to a "superior" level.

discrimination: treating a certain kind of people differently based on certain characteristics.

philanthropist: a person who loves humankind and engages in activities to improve the quality of human life.

Economic exploitation

After the explorers, the missionaries and the military, it was now the turn of the merchants and entrepreneurs to make their way to Africa.

The entrepreneurs built a transportation infrastructure, including canals, roads and railway lines, as well as infrastructure for extracting the natural resources, such as mines.

Africans were "hired," sometimes by force, to extract the natural resources. Many worked under conditions akin to slavery. Europeans thus acquired raw materials at low cost.

The Europeans did not build any industrial infrastructure (such as factories, textile mills, foundries, etc.) in the colonies. They processed the raw materials back in Europe, depriving Africans of any manufacturing jobs.

Many European countries imposed a colonial pact on their colonies, obliging them to trade only with the mother country. The colonies provided the mother country with raw materials at low prices, and then purchased back the manufactured goods at a price set by the mother country. Under this system, Europe gained complete control of world trade.

5.13 *Railway at the port of Matadi, in the Belgian Congo.*

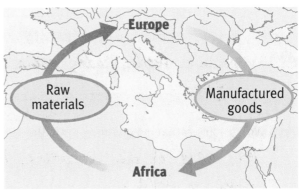

As people in the colonies were forced to buy European goods instead of those made by local artisans, the latter were put out of work. They had to seek work in the mines or the plantations, which were owned by the colonizers. The labour of Africans thus brought no economic benefit to their own countries: the economic benefit went to European countries instead.

 When a powerful country signs a trade agreement with a poor country today, which country is able to set terms most beneficial to itself? Why is this, do you think?

In 1914, Europe dominated the world economy, as the following statistics show:

Europe in the world economy

- Europe made half of the world's manufactured goods.
- Europe was involved in two thirds of the world's trade.
- Europe owned 80% of the world's merchant vessels, half of which were British.
- Europe owned 60% of the world's gold.

5.14 *Africans building a railway in Cameroon, 1905.*

pact: synonym for contract, or agreement.

Let's Get to Work!

1 Look up the definition of the word "Negro" in a dictionary.

a) Write down one of the definitions you have found, and any reference to usage.

Definition of Negro: A member of a dark-skinned group of peoples originally native to Africa south of the Sahara.

b) How does this definition differ from the one in Larousse's *Great Universal Dictionary of the 19th Century*? (see page 152).

The one in the 19th century was really offensive and mean. It made the word equal "bad" or "stupid"

c) Why is the definition different today?

Because people today realize that Black people are not inferior or different.

2 Would you say that most Europeans in the 19th century were philanthropists? Explain your answer.

Yes, many of the Europeans bought the idea of "civilizing" the black people in Africa.

3 Read this excerpt from the poem "The White Man's Burden" by British novelist Rudyard Kipling.

a) Find two adjectives that Kipling uses to describe Africans.

- *Fluttered, wild*
- _____

b) The line "bind your sons to exile" implies "send colonists to occupy faraway conquered lands."

In this poem, who seems to suffer most from colonization, the European colonists or the conquered populations? Explain your answer.

> Take up the White Man's burden—
> Send forth the best ye breed—
> Go bind your sons to exile
> To serve your captives' need;
> To wait in heavy harness,
> On fluttered folk and wild—
> Your new-caught, sullen peoples,
> Half-devil and half-child.
>
> Rudyard Kipling,
> *The White Man's Burden*, 1899.

The whites - they had to travel far away to lands with wild, ignorant people in order to civilise them. It wasl their duty ch people. because they have the burden or as a member of the "enlightened" race no mattar how Heavy a burden that wa.

... t of view? Explain your answer.

... e White people are doing horrible things to the Blacks.

4 Commodities come in two forms: raw materials and processed goods.

a) List the following commodities under the correct heading in the table below.

> metal • clothes • cotton • iron tools • diamonds • jewellery • wood • furniture

Raw materials		Processed goods	
Metal	diamonds	Clothes	jewellery
cotton	wood	Iron tools.	furniture

b) Which were produced by the colony and which by the mother country?

1. Raw materials: _colony_

2. Processed goods: _Mother Country_

c) If the Europeans had paid the Africans to extract the natural resources for them, would European manufacturers have made more or less profit? Check the correct answer.

☑ More profit

◯ Less profit

Why? _Because they would have had to pay them for their work._

5 Explain in your own words what was unfair about trade between Africa and Europe.

Firstly, the Europeans exploited the Africans for their natural resources. They forced the Africans to work for free. All the finished products were made in Europe.

6 If a Western country gives humanitarian aid to an African country, do you think it has the right to interfere in that country's domestic affairs? Why or why not?

No, Just because you give money doesn't give you the right to run the country.

7 a) Do you believe that every society in the world today should apply Western values, such as individual freedom, or freedom to do business?

No, if someone is happy with their life even if you disagree then that is their choice.

b) Do you think your opinion is similar or different from the opinions of 19th-century European colonizers?

No, they wanted everyone to be like them.

Resistance to colonization

In the late 19th century, some began to criticize Europe's domination of Africa.

In 1890, an African-American journalist wrote an open letter to Leopold II. Here are a few excerpts:

> ⭐ "Every charge which I am about to bring against your Majesty's Personal Government in the Congo has been carefully investigated ... Your Majesty's Government is excessively cruel to its prisoners, condemning them, for the slightest offenses, to the chain gang ... Your Majesty's Government is engaged in the slave trade. It buys and sells and steals slaves."
>
> George Washington Williams, *An Open Letter to His Serene Majesty Leopold II, King of the Belgians and Sovereign of the Independent State of Congo*, July 1890. From *King Leopold's Ghost*, by Adam Hochschild. New York: Houghton Mifflin Company, 1999.

Statements by Jules Ferry, a French politician who sang the praises of colonialism, were challenged by French parliamentarian Georges Clemenceau:

> "Superior races! Inferior races! So easy to say ... But no! The so-called superior races have no rights against the so-called inferior nations ... The conquest that you recommend is pure and simple exploitation. Our highly scientific civilization is exploiting elemental civilizations in order to take possession of their people, to torture them, and to extract every ounce of strength out of them for the benefit of the so-called civilizing power."
>
> Georges Clemenceau, Speech before the French Chamber of Deputies, July 30, 1885. Free translation.

There were protests in the colonies, too. Resistance movements sprang up all over the colonial world. The West African Samory Touré, for example, met European invaders with armed military resistance.

⭐ **SAMORY TOURÉ (1837 TO 1900)**

Samory Touré belonged to the Malinke people of West Africa. They were a Muslim people who traded in gold and raised livestock.

After getting involved in clan warfare in his country, Samory Touré discovered he was a gifted warrior, and became a military leader.

Touré was recognized as military chief by his people and formed a professional army equipped with firearms. This gradually enabled him to take control of an extensive empire. The Fulani, another West African people, proclaimed him *Almami*, a prestigious title given to some Muslim religious leaders.

When France and the United Kingdom began to colonize West Africa, Samory Touré tried to negotiate with them. But internal conflicts weakened his rule, and the French captured him in 1898. He died of pneumonia shortly afterwards.

5.15 *Africans fighting French invaders in French West Af*

Colonization in the early 20th century

Resistance and protests were not enough to slow down sweeping colonization. By 1914, the wave of colonization by the great industrial powers had transformed the map of the world, especially the map of Africa.

European states ruled over immense empires that stretched over several continents. For example,

– The French colonial empire covered 12 million square kilometres, or 20 times the area of France;
– The British colonial empire covered 29 million square kilometres, or 87 times the area of the United Kingdom.

5.16 *France and the United Kingdom dividing up Morocco and Egypt. Cartoon, circa 1908–14.*

5.17 COLONIES IN AFRICA IN **1914**

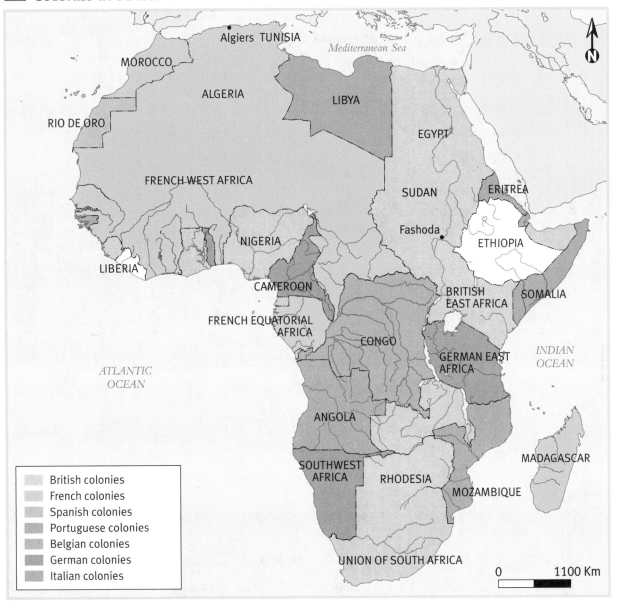

British colonies
French colonies
Spanish colonies
Portuguese colonies
Belgian colonies
German colonies
Italian colonies

Let's Get to Work!

E

1 Reread the excerpt from G.W. Williams's letter to Leopold II, King of Belgium (1st excerpt, page 156). Explain what, in Williams's view, the King of Belgium was doing that violated the Berlin Conference agreements.

King Leopold was forcing the congolese people into slavery which was illegal

2 What was the main strength of the European countries, according to Georges Clemenceau (2nd excerpt, page 156)?

Science

3 Why was the African warrior Samory Touré not able to stand up to France and the United Kingdom?

weakened rule due internal conflicts

4 Look at map 5.17 on page 157 and answer the questions.

a) Most of Africa was divided up between two European countries. Which two countries were they?

○ Germany
⊘ France ✓
⊘ United Kingdom ✓
○ Portugal

○ Italy
○ Belgium
○ Spain

b) What do you think other European countries thought about this division of Africa?

They thought it was unfair.

c) Generally speaking, which part of Africa did France control?

○ The centre
○ The south

○ The northeast
⊘ The northwest ✓

d) Generally speaking, which parts of Africa did the United Kingdom control?

○ The centre
⊘ The south ✓

⊘ The northeast ✓
○ The northwest

e) Which parts of Africa escaped European colonization?

Liberia, Ethiopia. ✓

5 Look at the cartoon (figure 5.16) on page 157. Why do you think the artist drew skeletons underneath the two soldiers?

To show the death of many Africans

6 How do you think Africa was divided up into countries?
Check the correct answer.

○ According to the African kingdoms that already existed

☑ According to agreements made among Europeans ✓

7 Indicate whether the following statements are true or false. If a statement is false, write the correct version underneath.

	TRUE	FALSE

a) The only opposition to colonization was in Africa. .... ○ .... ☒
United states and France

b) Samory Touré tried to resist the Europeans peacefully. .... ☒ .... ○✓
_____

c) Important Muslim leaders were given the title *Almami*. .... ☑ .... ○
_____

d) George W. Williams admired Leopold II's administration in the Congo. .... ○ .... ☑
He despised (hated)

8 Why do you think revolts by Africans against their colonizers might have been unsuccessful? Explain your answer.
Africans didn't stand a chance against the weapons of the Europeans.
_____
_____

9 a) Find out which European language is still spoken in the following African countries.

1. Senegal: _French_   4. Botswana: _English_

2. Kenya: _English_   5. Madagascar: _French_

3. Congo: _French_

b) Given your answers to part a), comment on the long-term effects of European presence in Africa.
They still speak the European languages and their religions
_____

10 Complete this crossword using the following definitions.

1. Continent that was almost entirely colonized in the 19th century.

2. American journalist who was opposed to colonization.

3. African who tried to resist colonization.

4. A country that colonized much of Africa.

```
           1
        2 W i L L i A m s
                  g
        3 T o u r e
                  i
        4 F r a n c e
                  a
```

欧洲帝国主义的影响是什么？

What Were the Effects of European Imperialism?

The colonization of Africa in the 19th century took place against the will of Africans, who were its first victims. The intense competition among rival European states wanting to rule Africa, or "the scramble for Africa," was one of the causes of the First World War, which broke out in 1914.

在非洲的影响

Effects on the Africans

Colonization brought Africans under the economic and cultural dominance of Europeans.

Economic effects 经济影响.

As you saw earlier, colonial trade discriminated against the colonies and brought profits to Europe at Africa's expense.

Colonization led to economic inequality between industrialized and non-industrialized countries:
– industrialized countries owned the manufacturing industries and possessed the wealth;
– non-industrialized countries were limited to extracting their natural resources; they were kept in poverty by industrialized countries.

When African colonies gained their freedom from the Europeans in the mid-20th century, they were left with no manufacturing infrastructure, no industry and no capital. African countries today are still feeling the effects of this economic discrimination, and are classified as "developing countries."

Cultural effects 文化影响.

Relations between Europeans and Africans led to acculturation. In other words, Africans adopted many aspects of European cultures, to the detriment of their own.

The acculturation of Africans took place in various ways:
– Many Africans converted to Christianity after learning about it from missionaries;
– Africans attended schools built by Europeans and learned the language, history and way of life of the mother country.

On the other hand, learning European languages and cultures enabled Africans to forge links of mutual aid and cooperation with their former colonizers. Today, for example, a collection of 50 French-speaking countries, mostly former French colonies, form an international association called the Francophonie. These countries are united by the French language, and organize cultural, economic and sporting events together. The Commonwealth is a similar organization that unites Britain's former colonies.

> Can you name some African countries where English is still spoken? French?

5.18 *European priest teaching African children in the early 20th century.*

Human and political effects

The colonization of the African continent resulted in the death of large numbers of Africans. Anyone who tried to resist was killed, and others died as a result of forced labour or cruel punishments. In addition, the colonizers passed laws that discriminated against the conquered peoples. A law in the Congo, for example, forbade blacks to live in the same neighbourhoods as whites.

The way Africa was carved up is at the origin of many conflicts still ravaging Africa today. Frontiers drawn by European powers took no account of the existing borders between African nations and kingdoms. One kingdom or ethnic group might end up scattered across several countries, while another ethnic group might end up occupying the same country as its enemy. This was the case with Congo-Brazzaville, a colony in French Equatorial Africa.

5.19 ETHNIC GROUPS OF CONGO-BRAZZAVILLE

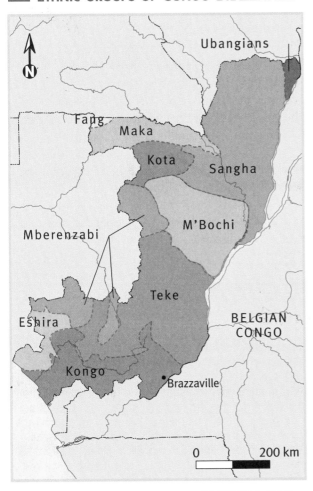

Do you know of a current conflict in Africa?

Effects on international relations

In spite of the agreement made at the Berlin Conference in 1885, European powers still fought over the division of Africa and other colonized lands. These conflicts led to international crises, especially among the United Kingdom, France and Germany.

Battles for control of the colonies

Two conflicts were particularly significant.

- In 1898, a dispute arose in Fashoda (see map 5.17, page 157) between the United Kingdom and France over the possession of Sudan. At stake was control of the Nile, the most important river in Africa. In the face of British military advantage, France eventually ceded Sudan to the United Kingdom. Soon afterwards the two countries signed the Entente Cordiale ("friendly agreement").

- From 1905 to 1906, and again in 1911, disputes arose between France and Germany over the possession of Morocco. The stakes were high, and the two countries failed to come to an agreement.

In 1913, the arms race in Germany, France and the United Kingdom began to intensify. Industrial development enabled them to manufacture arms in unprecedented quantities. German production relied heavily on the Krupp factories.

5.20 *Africans stood alongside French soldiers in the Fashoda crisis of 1898.*

The First World War

The First World War (1914–18) was fought between Germany and its allies Turkey (Ottoman Empire) and Austria-Hungary, on one side, and France, the United Kingdom, Japan and Russia on the other.

The war took place mostly in Europe, but also in some of the colonies, taking on global proportions. The colonies were involved in the war effort: France recruited hundreds of thousands of African soldiers, while the United Kingdom enlisted nearly a million Indians, 600,000 Canadians and 450,000 Australians and New Zealanders.

5.21 *Canadian soldiers fighting on a European battlefield in the First World War.*

Many thought the war would be over quickly, but it dragged on and on. When Russia was convulsed by a revolution at home in 1917, it withdrew from the conflict. That same year, the United States entered the war, lending economic and military support to the French and British Allies. The American presence tipped the balance in their favour and led to the defeat of Germany in 1918. A total of about ten million people lost their lives in this war, making it the bloodiest war in the history of the world up to that time.

With Germany defeated, the victors divided up its colonies among themselves.

The red poppy has become a memorial to American and Commonwealth soldiers who died during the First World War. In Canada it is worn on November 11, Remembrance Day, in memory of the 100,000 Canadian soldiers killed in action since the beginning of the 20th century.

In an attempt to prevent future wars, the victors created the League of Nations, an international organization dedicated to peace.

> What is the name of the international organization dedicated to world peace today?

Nationalism in the colonies

Many colonized people realized that the mother countries in Europe must be less powerful than they had imagined: Europe had needed its colonies during the war. Nationalist organizations began to emerge in several colonies, including Algeria and Tunisia.

Islamist movements also arose in some colonies. It seemed to many Africans that Islam was more respectful of their identity than Christianity, probably because it was not associated with such ruthless colonizers.

CAUSES OF THE FIRST WORLD WAR

Disputes over colonies was not the only cause of the First World War. On the eve of its outbreak, the political situation in Europe was explosive:

• European states had various alliances. Germany was allied with Turkey and Austria-Hungary, while the United Kingdom was allied with Russia and France. If a conflict erupted between two countries, all their allies were dragged into it too.

• France wanted to repossess the Alsace-Lorraine region, which Germany had taken from it in 1871.

• The United Kingdom and Germany were quarrelling over control of the North Sea.

• Germany was Europe's leading industrial power, but it had fewer colonies than the United Kingdom or France, and wanted more.

• The Ottoman Empire, founded by the Turks and made up of very diverse peoples and religions, began to come apart. New states emerged in the Balkans, such as Serbia, Bulgaria and Romania. These states began fighting with one another, and each allied itself to a greater European power. Russia, for example, backed Serbia, while Austria-Hungary backed Bulgaria. These were the regions where the war started.

Let's Get to Work!

1 Read the following passage about colonization in Algeria and then answer the questions.

> "In the vicinity of Algiers itself, the very fertile areas were torn from the hands of the Arabs and given to Europeans who, not being able or not wanting to cultivate them themselves, rented them to these same indigenous people, who thus became the mere farmers of the domains that had belonged to their fathers."
>
> Alexis de Tocqueville, *Report on the Bill on Special Funding Requested for Algeria*, 1847. From *Writings on Empire and Slavery*, translated and edited by Jennifer Pitts. Baltimore: Johns Hopkins University Press, 2001.

a) Who owned the land around Algiers before the Europeans arrived?

The Arabs

b) Who farmed the land before the Europeans arrived?

The Arabs

c) Who owned the land after colonization?

The Europeans

d) Who farmed the land after colonization?

The Arabs

e) If you were an Arab living in Algeria at this time, how would you feel about this situation?

The Arabs would have been every upset because their land was taken and now they have to work for their robbers.

2 Europeans used various means of propagating their culture in Africa.

a) How did they spread Christianity in Africa?

They sent missionaries

b) How did they transmit their languages and their values to Africans?

They built schools to teach their language.

3 South African Archbishop Desmond Tutu, who won the Nobel Peace Prize in 1984, said in a speech:

> "When the missionaries came to Africa they had the Bible and we had the land. They said 'Let us pray.' We closed our eyes. When we opened them, we had the Bible and they had the land."
>
> From *Desmond Tutu: A Biography*, by Stephen Gish. Westport, CT: Greenwood Press, 2004.

What did he mean by this? Explain in your own words.

The Europeans successfully tricked the Africans to getting exactly what they wanted (the land)

4 a) What effect did lack of industry have on Africa, in the long run?

Because they can't manufacture (make things) they can't get enough money to develop.

b) Among the following suggestions, which would be the most effective solutions to the problem of poverty in African countries?

○ Send Africans food from Canada

○ Build factories in Africa so they can process their natural resources

○ Establish technical colleges and universities in Africa

○ Sell Africans high-quality products made in Canada

c) Give reasons for the choices you made in part b).

if we build a factory in Africa they can develop their own products and sell it for a profit

5 Are the following statements true or false? If they are false, write the correct version underneath.

		TRUE	FALSE
a)	In the era of colonization, schools encouraged the learning of African languages.	○	✓

European

| b) | Europeans were full of admiration for African religions. | ○ | ✓ |

They hated their religion

| c) | African countries have kept links with their former colonizers. | ✓ | ○ |

True.

6 a) How did the colonies participate in the First World War?

Sent people to fight for the mother country.

b) What did the colonies demand from their mother countries, after the war?

Independence.

7 Write down one reason why Africans in many regions converted to Islam rather than to Christianity.

They wanted to convert because Christianity reminded them of the brutal past.

8 a) Write down at least two ways in which large numbers of Africans died under colonial rule.

• *Exhaustion, starvation. torture, amputation, etc...*

•

b) Was their situation similar or different to the situation of the indigenous people of America under colonization? Explain your answer.

Yes, it was very similar

9 Summarize the First World War by filling out this index card.

> **The First World War**
>
> Causes: _Fighting over the colonies in Africa, Germany wanted more land._
>
> _____
>
> _____
>
> Opposing forces:
>
> _Germany, Turkey, Austria, Hungary_ } Against { _French, UK, Japan and Russia._
>
> Total number of deaths: _10 million_
>
> Group of victorious countries: _France, UK, Japan and Russia_
>
> Consequence for conquered country: _they had to surrender their colonies._

10 Read this passage from the founding document of the League of Nations in 1919.

> "To those colonies and territories which, as a consequence of the late war, have ceased to be under the sovereignty of the States which formerly governed them, and which are inhabited by peoples not yet able to stand by themselves under the strenuous conditions of the modern world, there should be applied the principle that the well-being and development of such peoples form a sacred trust of civilization, and that securities for the performance of this trust should be embodied in this Covenant."
>
> Article 22, Covenant of the League of Nations, 1919.

a) What responsibilities did Western countries have towards African colonies, according to this statement?

_____

b) Highlight a phrase that shows that in 1919, when the League of Nations was founded, Westerners thought they were superior to Africans.

11 Use the following words to fill in the gaps in the passage below.

> industries • conflicts • religion • cultural • economic • political

During colonization, _economic_ relations between Africa and Europe were unequal, as the _industries_ and wealth remained in Europe. Europe had _cultural_ influence in many spheres, including language, _Religion_ and lifestyle. _conflicts_ broke out after the African continent was divided up. This was one of the most devastating _Political_ effects of colonization.

Was Japan an Imperialist State?

In the mid-19th century, while Europe was busy colonizing Africa and parts of Asia, Japan was undergoing a profound transformation. It emerged from this change as an industrial and imperialist world power.

European dominance

In about 1850, Europe and the United States took possession of many parts of Asia, just as Europeans had done in Africa. They forced independent countries such as Japan and China to sign unfair economic treaties. These treaties authorized Europeans to:
– conduct free trade in the ports of Asia;
– gain access to mineral and petroleum resources;
– build infrastructure such as railways.
Even though China and Japan were politically independent from Europe, profits from their natural resources went to European companies.

Japan's reaction

As you saw in Inquiry 1, Japan had been ruled by shoguns since 1603. Under the shoguns, Japan was closed to outside influence, and all trade with foreigners was forbidden.

The arrival of the Europeans led to clashes between those who believed Japan should remain isolated, on the one hand, and those who wanted it to modernize and open up to the outside world, on the other. The last shogun was unable to keep the peace. He resigned in 1867, ceding power to Emperor Mutsuhito.

Under Mutsuhito, Japan began to develop rapidly, both politically (creation of parliamentary institutions) and economically (industrial development). Europeans had taken centuries to reach the same level of development.

Japan managed to adopt certain Western ideas and technology, while at the same time asserting its independence and rejecting domination by foreign powers.

Political reform

In 1889, Emperor Mutsuhito adopted a constitution similar to European constitutions, establishing a division of power between the sovereign and parliament.

While retaining extensive powers, Mutsuhito administered the state along with elected representatives in parliament, which was divided into two houses, as in the United Kingdom. Newspapers and political parties with varying points of view emerged, opening the way for political debate.

Mutsuhito also established a state education system, based on competition, to educate the Japanese elite. The proportion of Japanese who were educated soon matched the rate in the most educated regions of Europe.

✳ EMPEROR MUTSUHITO (1852 TO 1912)

Mutsuhito succeeded his father as emperor in 1867, at the age of 15. He named Tokyo as the capital of Japan and abolished the shogunate, the system through which daimios and samurai had ruled Japan since 1603. This was the dawn of the Meiji period (*meiji* means "light" in Japanese), an era of profound reform characterized by the adoption of Western-style institutions and technology.

✳ Mutsuhito named Shinto the state religion, thereby rejecting Buddhism. The Shinto religion, practised only in Japan, symbolized cultural and linguistic unity in the face of foreign influence.

Industrialization in Japan

Traditionally, the Japanese economy was based largely on the silk trade. At the beginning of the Meiji period, in the mid-19th century, Japan transformed its economy by developing European-style industries. It built foundries, cotton mills, railways and steamboats. It called on Western skills to develop its industries, hiring experts to train the Japanese in modern industrial European techniques.

5.22 *Textile factory, circa 1925. The workers are using looms made in America.*

Is Japan still a highly industrialized nation?

Japanese imperialism

Japan's major achievement in the Meiji period was to sign egalitarian treaties with Western countries. These treaties guaranteed that trade would benefit both signatories equally. This was the first time Europe had ever negotiated on an equal footing with a non-Western country.

✷ Mutsuhito built up an impressive army and navy modelled on European forces and technology. Then Japan began to expand its territory, in imitation of imperialist Europe. It needed raw materials, cultivable land, and colonies of settlement where Japan's surplus population could go and live. Japan took control of the coastal areas of the Sea of Japan, at times clashing with other world powers that claimed these areas for themselves.

These conflicts led to war:
- in 1894–95, Japan defeated the Chinese army and took possession of Formosa (now Taiwan);
- in 1904–05, Japan fought with Russia over the territories north of the Sea of Japan. Japan once again triumphed, taking control of Korea, southern Sakhalin and Port Arthur.

Japan also took part in the First World War, fighting alongside the United Kingdom and France, which entitled it to the spoils of war in 1919. This is how it came to occupy the Mariana, Marshall and Caroline islands in the Pacific Ocean, formerly German colonies.

5.23 THE JAPANESE EMPIRE IN 1910

Japan in 1868
Territories won from China (1894–95)
Territories won from Russia (1905 and 1910)

RUSSIAN EMPIRE
SAKHALIN
Vladivostok
Beijing
KOREA *Sea of Japan*
Port Arthur
Seoul
JAPAN Tokyo
CHINA
Shanghai
East China Sea
0   530 km
PACIFIC OCEAN
Hong Kong
FORMOSA (TAIWAN)
Mariana, Caroline and Marshall Islands

✷ TINTIN AND *THE BLUE LOTUS*

In 1929, Belgian comic artist and writer Hergé created the famous character Tintin, a reporter who has countless adventures with his dog, Snowy. The action of *The Blue Lotus* takes place in China in the 1930s, during Japanese colonization. Hergé also depicts Europeans in China, who enjoyed a privileged lifestyle and despised Asians.

---

spoils: goods or property seized by a victor in wartime.

Let's Get to Work!

1 Write down five changes that Emperor Mutsuhito brought about in Japan.

- _____
- _____
- _____
- _____
- _____

2 a) Indicate whether the following treaties were equal or unequal:

1. The treaties between Europe and Japan during the Meiji period: _____

2. The treaties between Europe and Africa: _____

b) Is Japan today

○ an industrialized country?

☑ a developing country?

c) How do you explain the difference between Japan's current economic situation and that of African countries?

_____

_____

3 Indicate whether the following statements apply to European imperialism in Africa or to Japanese imperialism in the Sea of Japan, or to both.

	European imperialism	Japanese imperialism
The scramble for colonies led to armed conflict.		
The need for raw materials was a motive for colonization.		
Colonization meant surplus populations could emigrate from the mother country.		
The conquered lands were far from the mother country.		
Colonization was based on racial discrimination.		

4 Why do you think industrialization happened more quickly in Japan than in Europe?

_____

_____

_____

5 a) Make a list of everything that Japan borrowed from Western culture and technology.

_____

_____

b) What two distinct aspects of its culture has Japan kept to this day?

- _____

- _____

6 a) In the light of what you have learned in this Inquiry so far, draw arrows matching each of these concepts with the correct definition.

CONCEPT	DEFINITION
1. Discrimination	Movement by a people to achieve recognition as a separate nation
2. Nationalism	One people adopting various cultural expressions of another people
3. Acculturation	Treating a group of people differently from other groups

b) What word best describes Japan's reaction to Europe attempting to colonize it? Check the correct answer.

○ Discrimination   ○ Nationalism   ○ Acculturation

c) Explain your answer to part b).

_____

_____

7 On the timeline below, locate the following events:

a) European and American occupation of Asian territories

b) Start of shogun rule

c) Resignation of last shogun

d) First Japanese constitution

Don't forget to mark years on the timeline.

Synthesis Activities

E 1 Read this account of the colonization of Algeria. Using the following words, write down next to each event the concept that best describes it.

> discrimination • nationalist resistance • acculturation • colonization • military conquest

FRENCH COLONIZATION OF ALGERIA

a) The French landed in Algeria in 1830. They arrived in 500 ships carrying 35,000 soldiers.

Military conquest

b) They clashed with troops led by Abd el-Kader, a Muslim leader who opposed the French invasion.

Nationalist resistance

c) In 1847, Abd el-Kader was defeated after many years of fighting. French colonists settled in Algeria. They cultivated the land and built bridges and railways to assert their authority in the territory.

Colonization

d) France built schools in Algeria. If Algerians abandoned certain Muslim practices, such as polygamy, they could become French citizens.

Acculturation

e) In 1881, France imposed repressive laws on Algerians. They were forbidden to move around at night, subjected to forced labour and obliged to pay taxes and duties.

Discrimination

2 a) Indicate whether each of the following statements applies to the mother country or the colony.

	Mother country	Colony
It processes resources into manufactured goods.	✓	
Natural resources are extracted for export.		✓
It holds the main decision-making powers.	✓	
Colonists settle here and build a transportation infrastructure.	✓	
Laws are passed here that discriminate against indigenous people.		✓
It is impoverished by the world economy.		✓
It adopts other people's languages and customs.		✓
It believes it belongs to a superior civilization.	✓	
Its investors finance voyages of discovery to Africa.	✓	
It profits from the world economy.	✓	
It has no factories.		✓

b) In which continent were most of the mother countries situated, in the early 20th century?

Europe

c) Name a continent in which there were many colonies by the early 20th century.

Africa.

3 Complete the following outline using information you have learned in this Inquiry.

EUROPEAN IMPERIALISM IN AFRICA

Motives

Economic motives:

The were looking for raw materials to turn into manufactured goods

Social motives:

They wanted to convert everyone to christianity and to learn their languages

Political motives:

The more land they could possess would mean the more power they had

Stages

1. Exploration of the continent

Names of four explorers:

Henry Morton Stanley

David Livingstone

Rene Caillie

Pierre Savorgnan de Brazza

Heinrich Barth

Exploration routes:

River and lakes

Conflict resolution in 1884:

Berlin Conference

2. Colonization

Economic activities:

Mines, Railroads, ports

Cultural activities:

schools and churches

Effects on Africans

Discrimination

slavery

Slavery.

Torture

High death rate

stole their land

Acculturation

Poverty

Economic dependence.

4 a) How did Africans try to resist colonization?

Some African nations tried to resist such as Samoury Toure. He fought against the Europeans both peacefully and violently and lost both times.

b) Did they manage to resist colonization?

No, they were always defeated because they didn't have he weapons needed to win

5 International relations in the colonial era were affected by many events.

a) In what year did the following events occur?

1. Conflict over Morocco: _1905 - 1906 - 1911_

2. First World War: _1914 - 1918_

3. War between Japan and Russia: _1904 - 1905_

4. Berlin Conference: _1884 - 1885_

5. Fashoda Crisis: _1898_

6. War between Japan and China: _1894 - 1895_

b) Locate these events on the timeline below. Don't forget to mark years on the timeline.

c) What was the common cause of all these events?

They are all about colonization

6 The following are two of the problems facing Africa today. What do you think caused each of these problems?

a) Africa is poor and lacks industries.

Cause: _They don't have any factories wich can manufacture finished products._

b) African countries are torn apart by internal crises and civil wars, as many ethnic groups fight for power.

Cause: _The Europeans divided the land but the Africans didn't like how they did it and are fighting each other to get it back._

7 Explain imperialism in your own words.

When a stronger more powerful country takes over a weaker country and exploits its people and resources.

Synthesis Activities

8 Do you think that industrial countries should help Africa recover from its extreme poverty? Should young Europeans of your age be held responsible for what their ancestors did in Africa? Explain your point of view.

Yes, we should help Africa because it's the right thing to do. Nobody should suffer and if we can teach them to do. Nobody should suffer and if we should.

—No, young people should not be responsible for other people's actions.

9 a) Reorganize these letters into words.

OCNYLO   C o l o n y
                     8

ORHMET YTUCONR   M o t h e r   c o u n t r y
                  2   4

TICNARSIIDOINM   D i s c r i m i n a t i o n
                  10   5   11

TANASMILNOI   n a t i o n a l i s m
                     6

CUUNIRTATLACO   A c c u l t u r a t i o n
                          7 1

TIENIOTOPXAL   E x p l o i t a t i o n
                  3   9

b) Transfer the numbered letters to the boxes below to find the mystery word that is key to this Inquiry. Then use the words you found in part a) to complete the conceptual diagram below.

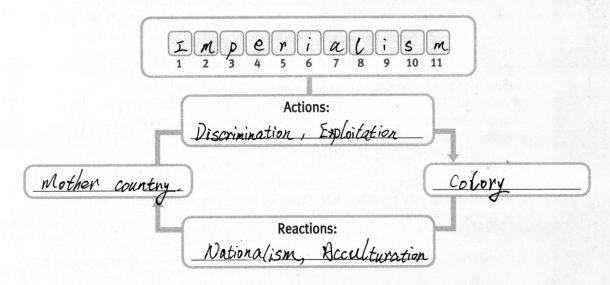

I m p e r i a l i s m
1 2 3 4 5 6 7 8 9 10 11

Actions:
Discrimination, Exploitation

Mother country

Colony

Reactions:
Nationalism, Acculturation

Inquiry Conclusion

SUMMARIZE WHAT YOU HAVE LEARNED

Use the following words to write a short text explaining the effects of European imperialism on African populations.

mother country • colony • discrimination • acculturation • industrialization • raw material • capital • evangelize • nationalism

mother country: A more powerful country with colonies under its control.
Colony: A country that was taken over by another more powerful country.
Discrimination: Not being treated fairly based on skin color or religion
Acculturation: to take someone else's culture
Industrialization: To use machines instead of by hand.
Raw material: From nature
Capital: To raise money to invest in a business
Evangelize: covert religion
nationalism: patriotic feeling, principles, or efforts.

RETURN TO THE SECTION "ON THE TRAIL"

Return to pages 140 and 141 and reread your responses to the questions asked. Reassess them in the light of what you have learned since. Then try to answer the two questions that you wrote down on page 141. If you cannot, try to figure out why.

Discuss and Take a Stand

In the colonial era, Western countries imposed their cultures and values on their colonies. Today, colonization is criticized for the wrongs it inflicted on colonized peoples. But how do we who live in rich industrialized countries behave towards countries in Africa and Asia today? We call poor countries "developing countries," suggesting that we are more developed than they are, and that they should follow our example. Western countries, including Canada, try to transmit and sometimes impose their own values, such as democracy and freedom to conduct business, on the rest of the world. This attitude shows that Westerners still believe, to a great extent, that their civilization is superior to others. What do you think about this? Do we have the right to impose our values on other peoples?

TC Your teacher will give you a worksheet including questions and illustrations as clues. Try to answer the questions using the visual clues. Then discuss your answers with your classmates.

On the Trail

In Western societies today, the law guarantees the same rights to all persons, whatever their sex, race, ethnic origin or religion. This was not always the case: until the middle of the 20th century, some groups were considered inferior, and treated as such. These groups had to struggle to win equal rights.

Look at the illustrations on these two pages and then answer the questions.

6.1 *Martin Luther King was a passionate defender of the rights of black Americans in the 1960s.*

"I would be the first to advocate obeying just laws. One has not only a legal but a moral responsibility to obey just laws. Conversely, one has a moral responsibility to disobey unjust laws."

Letter written in prison by Martin Luther King, 1963.
From *Why We Can't Wait* by Martin Luther King and Jesse Jackson.
New York: New American Library, 2000.

6.2 *In the 1950s, people thought that a woman's place was in the home.*

In the mid-20th century, what rights do you think were denied to blacks? To women?

_____
_____
_____
_____

How do you think these rights were won?

_____
_____
_____
_____

6.3 *In the 1940s, millions of Jews, including men, women and children, were killed in Nazi concentration camps.*

Maldives – Jennifer Latheef, imprisoned for exercising freedom of expression

"Jennifer Latheef, a photographer with the daily Minivan News and a human rights activist, was sentenced to 10 years in prison on 18 October for a supposed "terrorist act," of throwing a stone at a policeman during a demonstration in Malé on 20 September against the death of five prisoners while being tortured. Five other protesters were given long jail sentences. She has denied throwing any stones and said she was at the demonstration gathering information about victims of repression … Her father, Mohamed Latheef, is the main leader of the democratic opposition and is in exile in Sri Lanka."

Reporters Without Borders,
November 4, 2005.

Why were the people mentioned above deprived of their freedom?

_____

_____

_____

_____

_____

Write down two questions that come to mind about the struggle for rights and freedoms.

• _____

_____

_____

• _____

_____

_____

20世纪公民权利获胜的 背景是什么?

What Was the Context of the Winning of Civil Rights in the 20th Century?

Growth in the industrialized countries was in full swing in the mid-20th century. At that time, however, the whole world was shaken by two major crises. These crises helped create the conditions for decolonization, as well as the birth of movements for the recognition of civil rights in many countries.

The economic crisis 降低 经济危机.

The entire industrialized world was shaken by an economic crisis that began in 1929. On October 24 of that year, there was a massive sell-off of shares by investors in the United States. As a result, share prices on the New York Stock Exchange dropped dramatically. In the panic that followed, all investors wanted to sell their shares. But as they could find no buyers, prices dropped even further. Companies were starved for capital, and many of them went bankrupt overnight. 大萧条,

This stock market crash marked the beginning of a severe economic crisis. It lasted for 10 years, from 1929 to 1939, and is known as the Great Depression of the 1930s.

Share prices fall on the stock exchange 股票价格涨在交易所

↓

Businesses go bankrupt and close 企业破产.

↓

Workers lose their jobs 以失业   更多企业碎和关闭 More businesses go bankrupt and close

↓

Unemployed people no longer buy goods 失业的人再购买商品.

Because all countries traded with one another, the Depression soon spread to the entire world. Industrialized countries, which had grown spectacularly since the Industrial Revolution, were especially hard hit. The Depression showed just how fragile the capitalist system and economic liberalism were.

6.4 *A soup kitchen for the unemployed in Montreal in the 1930s.*

The Great Depression of the 1930s

- Global production fell by 30% between 1929 and 1933
- Countries abandoned free trade and returned to protectionism
- World trade fell by two thirds
- Many people were unemployed (almost 25% of the labour force in the United States)

The Depression also destabilized democratic governments. It created favourable conditions for the rise of authoritarian political systems, which proposed drastic solutions to the problems brought about by the Depression:
– government control of the economy;
– establishment of a powerful army;   破坏
– a ban on unions and strikes;   的稳
– a ban on criticizing the government.

The end of the Depression coincided with the outbreak of the Second World War in 1939. Industries related to war began to revitalize the economies of industrialized countries.

civil rights: rights guaranteed to all citizens by law.

bankrupt: said of a company that can no longer meet its payments.

protectionism: measures such as tariffs and import quotas aimed at protecting a country's industries from foreign competition.

The Second World War

After the First World War (1914–18), the victors imposed harsh conditions on defeated Germany in a treaty signed at Versailles, near Paris, in 1919.

Treaty of Versailles 限局.

- Germany had to pay reparations to compensate the victors for their losses.
- Germany had to abolish military service.
- Germany did not have the right to rearm.
- Germany gave up territory in Europe along with all its colonies.

6.5 *Many European cities were destroyed during the war.*

These requirements were one of the causes of the Second World War. The impact of the Depression was especially severe in Germany, whose economy was highly dependent on the United States. Frustrated at living in poverty, and humiliated by the harsh conditions the Allies had imposed on them, the Germans voted Adolf Hitler's National Socialist (or Nazi) party into power. The Nazis abolished democracy in Germany and established an authoritarian regime.

Hitler decided to rearm his country despite the ban imposed by the Allies in the Treaty of Versailles. In September 1939, Germany invaded Poland. France and the United Kingdom responded by declaring war on Germany. Two opposing camps, the Axis and the Allies, took shape.
- Axis powers: Germany, Italy, Japan (authoritarian governments).
- Allied powers: France and the United Kingdom, and then later, the USSR (Russia) and the United States (democratic governments except for the USSR).

Colonies and former colonies, such as Canada, Australia, India, New Zealand and South Africa, sent troops and provisions in support of the Allies. Battles between Axis and Allied forces took place in several regions of the world: not only in Europe, but also in Asia, Africa and the Middle East.

The climax of the war came on August 6, 1945, when the United States dropped the world's first atomic bomb on the city of Hiroshima, Japan. The city was levelled and hundreds of thousands of people died. The war ended soon afterwards with an allied victory. Cities and a great deal of infrastructure (roads, bridges, railways, etc.) were destroyed. Between 50 million and 60 million people were killed in the war, or about 2% of the world's population at the time. It was the first war in which a majority of the people killed were civilians.

The creation of the United Nations 联合国的创立.

The League of Nations had failed to maintain peace. In 1945, to prevent a new world war from occurring, the Allies replaced the League of Nations with a new organization, the United Nations (UN).

The UN Charter contained the mandate that the Allies gave to the United Nations. It reflected the basic values of the Allied countries, most of which were democratic.

The UN's mandate in the world

- To foster peace, security and cooperation
- To promote respect for human rights
- To improve people's living conditions

The UN has created numerous organizations. In 1957, for example, it established the International Atomic Energy Agency, whose mission is to oversee the peaceful use of nuclear energy.

6.6 *The UN emblem.*

civilian: person who is not in the armed forces.
charter: document that states a fundamental law.
mandate: role or task assigned to a person or organization.

✳ THE UNIVERSAL DECLARATION OF HUMAN RIGHTS

In 1948, the UN adopted the Universal Declaration of Human Rights. Here are some excerpts.

"Article 1

All human beings are born free and equal in dignity and rights.

Article 2

1. Everyone is entitled to all the rights and freedoms set forth in this Declaration, without distinction of any kind, such as race, colour, sex, language, religion, political or other opinion, national or social origin, property, birth or other status.

Article 20

1. Everyone has the right to freedom of peaceful assembly and association.

Article 21

1. Everyone has the right to take part in the government of his country ...

2. Everyone has the right of equal access to public service in his country.

Article 23

2. Everyone, without any discrimination, has the right to equal pay for equal work."

Universal Declaration of Human Rights, 1948.

6.7 THE 51 MEMBER COUNTRIES OF THE UN IN 1945

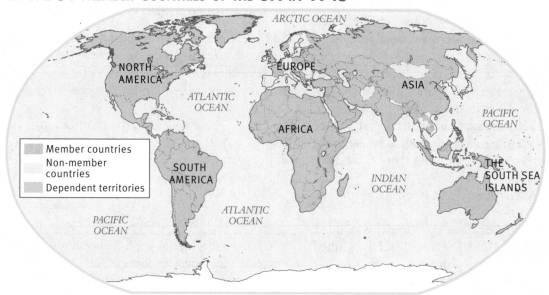

Today, more than 190 countries, representing 99% of the world's population, are members of the United Nations.

6.8 MOVEMENTS FOR RECOGNITION OF CIVIL RIGHTS AND FREEDOMS

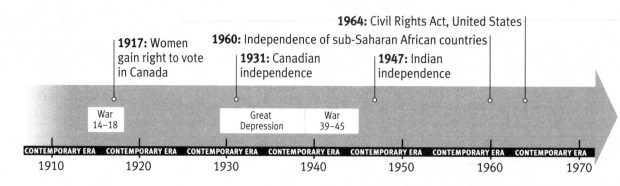

Let's Get to Work!

1 In an economic system in which prices are based on supply and demand, what happens to share prices on the stock exchange

a) when many investors want to buy shares?

☑ Prices rise

☐ Prices fall

b) when many investors want to sell shares?

○ Prices rise

☑ Prices fall

2 Name a commodity whose price varies on international markets.

Countries abandoned free trade and returned to protectionism.

gas, oil, diamonds, gold.

3 Since the Great Depression of the 1930s, Western countries have introduced mechanisms to limit the harmful effects of economic crises.

a) Do you think a worker in Canada who lost his or her job would have no income? Explain your answer.

~~Yes.~~ No, we have government programs such as unemployment and welfare.

b) Explain how your answer to part a) would change the diagram on page 178.

Companies might not have all gone bankrupt, fewer suicides, less hard on people.

4 The solutions that authoritarian governments imposed to solve the economic crisis of the 1930s did not respect basic freedoms. Use arrows to match each solution with the freedom that it violated.

a) Government control of the economy   Freedom of expression

b) Ban on trade unions   Freedom of association

c) Ban on criticizing the government   Freedom to conduct business

5 In 1939, why did the Great Depression end?

Because of World War 2.

6 Name at least two causes of the Second World War.

- *Germany had to pay reparations to compensate the victors for their losses*

- *Germany had to abolish military service.*

The great depression Germany did not respect the Treaty of Versailles, Authoritarian. government of Germany (aka Hitler) invasion of poland.

7 a) What kind of political system did most of the countries that won the Second World War have? Check the correct answer.

◯ Authoritarian system   ☑ Democratic system

b) Which of the following values is most important in that kind of system? Check the correct answer.

☑ Freedom   ◯ Authority

◯ Discipline   ◯ Power

8 Which part of the UN's mandate does each of the following statements correspond to? Check the correct answers.

	Foster peace, security and cooperation	Promote respect for human rights	Improve people's living conditions
Rich countries should support poor countries to avoid extreme economic disparities.			✓
The UN tries to persuade all countries to adopt the values of freedom and democracy.	✓		
Countries should use peaceful means (economic sanctions, diplomacy, etc.) in response to acts of aggression by one country against another.	✓		
In 1948, the UN established the World Health Organization.			✓
In 1945, the UN established the International Court of Justice.		✓	
In 1957, the UN established the International Atomic Energy Agency.		✓	

9 In 1948, which article of the Universal Declaration of Human Rights do you think colonized peoples might have used to demand their independence? Explain your answer.

~~Af~~ Article 21 because people should fight and vote for people of their own country.

10 Look at map 6.7, on page 180. On which continent were most of the countries that were not founding members of the UN? Why, do you think? Use map 5.17, on page 157, to help you answer.

Africa, because they used to the colonies of Europe.

Project

It is only fairly recently that women in Quebec have won equal rights. Fifty years ago, the status of women in Quebec was very different than it is now.

Task: In this Inquiry, we invite you to find out about how women in Quebec have won their rights and freedoms over the years, up to the present.

Final product required: A newspaper article reporting on an interview with a woman in her fifties or older, on the status of women now and in the past.

Several steps are necessary to complete the project. Use the Project Planning Guide [TC] that your teacher will give you.

1 Find a woman you know who is at least 50 years old and ask her if you can interview her about changes in the status of women in Quebec (or elsewhere) that she has experienced since her childhood. The interview can be with a relative or any other woman who agrees to be interviewed.

2 Write down a list of questions. They should cover several subjects, such as working conditions for women, access to education, relations between men and women, marriage, gender roles within families, etc. Ask your interviewee what the situation was like when she was young, and how it has changed since then.

3 For the interview, choose a quiet place where you won't be disturbed. Take notes on your interviewee's answers or, if she is willing, record the interview.

4 Write an article reporting on the interview, with emphasis on changes in the status of women in Quebec (or elsewhere) in recent decades.

How Did Decolonization Happen? 非殖民化是如何发生的.

European countries were weakened by the Great Depression of the 1930s. After the damage caused by war, they began to lose interest in their colonies and concentrated on their own reconstruction. At the same time, people in the colonies demanded that their mother countries recognize their war effort by granting them independence.

The causes of decolonization 非殖民代的原因.

In the postwar years, mother countries granted independence to their colonies. This is the process known as decolonization. Decolonization was the result of a number of factors.

Factors relating to the colonies 与殖民地有关的因素	Factors relating to the mother countries 与母
• Colonized peoples no longer wanted to submit to political leaders in the mother countries, because they had no representatives there to protect their interests.	• Weakened by the war, Europe no longer had the means to maintain the military occupation of its colonies.
• People in the colonies were frustrated that the great powers did not recognize the important role of the colonies in the Allied victory of 1945.	• Europe needed to rebuild its own infrastructure and therefore no longer had the means to maintain infrastructure in the colonies.
• The 1948 Universal Declaration of Human Rights was a source of support for people in the colonies, as it stated that all people had the same rights.	• The USSR and the United States encouraged some nationalist movements in the colonies to expand their influence in the world.
• There was a domino effect: the independence of some colonies encouraged others to demand their own independence.	• There was a change in attitudes: after the war, intellectuals and religious leaders were increasingly critical of colonialism and supported the nationalist demands of people in the colonies.

Indian independence 印度独立.

India had been a British colony since the early 19th century. In the 1920s, two men came to embody the struggle for independence: Jawaharlal Nehru and Mohandas Gandhi. During the Second World War, the United Kingdom promised India independence in exchange for the colony's support for the Allied cause. After the Allied victory, India thus became an independent country, with Nehru as prime minister.

✳ MOHANDAS KARAMCHAND GANDHI (1869 TO 1948)

Gandhi is regarded as India's spiritual leader and the founding father of independent India. He was an advocate of nonviolent revolution. After studying law in Britain, he began practising law in South Africa in 1893.

After returning to India in 1914, he became involved in the Indian National Congress along with Jawaharlal Nehru. He encouraged Indians to resist British occupation through nonviolent actions: he urged Indian employees of the government to resign, parents to withdraw their children from public schools and the population in general to boycott British products. He also organized peaceful demonstrations. Although he was arrested many times, Gandhi always preached nonviolence. He was assassinated by a Hindu extremist in 1948.

Gandhi (left) with Nehru in 1935.

---

boycott: to refuse to buy goods or services from a particular company or country.

The decolonization of Africa 非洲州的解殖民化

After the Second World War, France did not tolerate the presence of nationalist movements in its colonies. In some regions of Africa, nationalist activists were put in jail or expelled from their countries. In Madagascar, France responded to independence movements with repression that left tens of thousands of people dead. France's attitude led to its involvement in some bloody conflicts, especially in Asia, where it lost Indochina in 1954 after a nine-year war.

After this, France decided to negotiate with its colonies.

- In 1956, it granted independence to Tunisia and Morocco.
- Also in 1956, it granted a degree of autonomy to its colonies in sub-Saharan Africa (French Equatorial Africa and French West Africa), allowing them to elect African representatives to the colonial government.
- In 1960, France's colonies in sub-Saharan Africa and Madagascar became completely independent countries and full members of the United Nations.

Newly independent countries 新独立的的國家.

Since 1945, 80 countries that were previously colonies have become members of the UN. Most of these countries are in the Third World.

In 1960, the UN adopted a Declaration on the Granting of Independence to Colonial Countries and Peoples, which stated that
- all peoples have the right to self-determination, and colonialism must be brought to an end;
- colonialism is contrary to the UN Charter because it threatens world peace and cooperation.

In 1945, 750 million people lived in colonized countries. This figure had declined to under 2 million by 2006. Most of the countries that are not independent are islands.

✷ Many of the new countries were torn between their own cultures and the cultures of their former mother countries, to which they remained attached. This tension is illustrated in the following passage by the writer Léopold Sédar Senghor, who became the first president of the Republic of Senegal in 1960. Senghor was a promoter of African civilization, but at the same time was attached to the Francophonie:

> "The fact is that I believe, first and foremost, in the Negro-African culture, or Négritude, in its expression through poetry and the arts ... I also believe in the Francophonie, for the future ... where Négritude has already begun to play its primordial role."
>
> Léopold Sédar Senghor, *Ce que je crois*, Paris: B. Grasset, 1988. Free translation.

✷ HABIB BOURGUIBA (1903 TO 2000)

Habib Bourguiba, the leader of Tunisia's struggle for independence, was initially a lawyer and then a journalist before founding a nationalist political party, the Neo Destour. In the period when France repressed nationalist movements, he was thrown in jail, but he continued his struggle against French occupation.

During the Second World War, he supported the Allies against Germany. As a result, after the war he was able to gain support for the Tunisian national cause all over the world – even in France.

In 1956, Tunisia became independent and Bourguiba was elected its first president. He held office for 30 years, until 1987. He contributed to the modernization of his country by allowing women to play a more important role and by replacing Islamic religious law with secular law.

---

repression: use of violence against a rebel movement.
Indochina: region of Asia comprising Laos, Cambodia and Vietnam.

Third World: synonym for developing countries.
self-determination: right of a people to govern themselves.

Let's Get to Work!

1 Use the following words to fill in the gaps in the text below.

> UN • nationalist • weakened • second • independence • countries •
> superior • charter • mother countries • civilizations • colonies

After the ___second___ World War, the ___mother countries___ of Europe gradually granted independence to their ___colonies___ in Africa and Asia. They were pressured into doing this, in part because of ___nationalist___ movements that demanded more autonomy. Europe had been ___weakened___ by the war, and had needed its colonies to help in the fight. It could no longer claim to be ___superior___ to other ___civilizations___. When the ___UN___ was established, it adopted a ___charter___ of human rights, which encouraged peoples that were dominated by others to demand their ___independence___. Since then, 80 new independent ___countries___ have been established.

2 How did decolonization happen in the following regions?

	THROUGH WAR	THROUGH NEGOTIATION
a) French sub-Saharan Africa	○	☑
b) Indochina	☑	○
c) India	○	☑
d) Tunisia	○	☑

3 Do you think the right to self-determination is an individual or collective right? Explain your answer.

I think those two are right. Because collective interests and personal interests are interdependent. Only by safeguarding collective interests can individual interests be guaranteed. Collective, because it takes many,

4 a) Who do you think wrote the passage below? Give reasons for your answer. to make a change

> "Nonviolence is the greatest force at the disposal of humanity. It is mightier than the mightiest weapon of destruction devised by the ingenuity of humanity."

Gandhi.

b) Do you agree with this point of view? Why? Because he was an advocate for peace and Yes, I agree with this point of view. Because if we an eye for an eye ends up only making the whole world blind. Not using violence is the limit of humility. if we can develop willpower, we will find that we no longer need the armed forces.

5 Explain how independence represented progress for the rights of peoples in the former colonies.

All people have the right to self-determination.

It shows that Africa can make it on their own. They can support their own country and run their own government without "whites" telling them what to do.

6 a) Name at least one thing Gandhi did to bring about Indian independence.

He was an advocate of nonviolent revolution.

He told parents to pull their children from "English" school, stop buying British products.

b) Name at least two things Habib Bourguiba did to bring about Tunisian independence.

• *allowing women to play a more important role and*
  He support the allies against germany.

• *replacing Islamic religious law with secular law.*
  He started a nationalist party.

E 7 Compare the statement by Léopold Sédar Senghor (page 185) with the one by Jules Ferry (Inquiry 5, page 152).

a) Explain what each of these men thought of African civilization.

Léopold Sédar Senghor:

He thought they were the same as everyone else. He loved them.

Jules Ferry:

Hated Black people thought them they were uncivilized.

b) What impact do you think Senghor's words would have had on Africans, who had been colonized for centuries?

They have always retained the original culture and ideas.

E 8 Read the passage below, in which France declared its recognition of Tunisia's independence in 1956. Highlight the words indicating that, as of 1956, France would treat its former colony as an equal.

"France solemnly recognizes the independence of Tunisia ... Respecting each other's sovereignty, France and Tunisia agree to define or complete the modalities of their interdependence, freely worked out between the two countries, by organizing their cooperation in areas where they have common interests, especially in the areas of defence and foreign relations."

Protocol of Agreement between France and Tunisia, March 20, 1956. Free translation.

How Did the Movement to End Racial Discrimination Arise?

Dossier

From the 16th century on – that is, from the beginning of colonization and the slave trade – whites discriminated against blacks. After the Second World War, blacks in the United States and South Africa began to demand equality with whites.

The civil rights movement 美国的民权运动 in the United States

Even though slavery had been abolished in 1865, and the Constitution now recognized civil rights for blacks, in the mid-20th century several American states still had discriminatory laws: interracial marriages were forbidden, blacks were not allowed to attend the same schools as whites, etc.

In many of the southern states, blacks were denied the right to vote, and secret societies, such as the Ku Klux Klan, terrorized and killed blacks.

In the mid-20th century, all over the United States, blacks lived in poorer conditions than whites:
- infant mortality was twice as high among blacks as among whites;
- blacks were half as likely as whites to finish high school;
- the unemployment rate was twice as high among blacks as among whites;
- the vast majority of blacks could not obtain a loan to buy a house.

6.9 *Ku Klux Klan ceremony, 1986.*

After the Second World War, in which many black Americans participated, a black civil rights movement took shape. Leaders such as Martin Luther King preached the use of nonviolent **dissidence** to achieve the movement's goals. Other groups took violent action, such as the Black Muslims, of whom Malcolm X is the most famous, and the Black Panthers.

 Where do black Americans come from?

✳ **MARTIN LUTHER KING (1929 TO 1968)** 马·路德金.

Martin Luther King, a Baptist minister, was inspired by Gandhi's nonviolence. He fought for the right to vote, to high-quality jobs and to equality with whites. King was awarded the Nobel Peace Prize in 1964. In 1968 he was assassinated.

In 1963, during the March on Washington for Jobs and Freedom, he delivered a speech that became famous. The following is an extract:

"I have a dream that my four little children will one day live in a nation where they will not be judged by the colour of their skin but by the content of their character ... I have a dream that one day ... little black boys and black girls will be able to join hands with little white boys and white girls and walk together as sisters and brothers."

---

dissidence: a synonym for rebellion or revolt.

now... Did you know... Did you know...

ROSA PARKS (1913 to 2005)

Rosa Parks was a black seamstress in Montgomery, Alabama, where she was active in civil rights organizations. In December 1955, she refused to give up her seat on a bus to a white passenger, in violation of a city ordinance. She was arrested and ordered to pay a fine.

This incident touched off a far-reaching protest movement. Martin Luther King organized a boycott of the bus company, as a result of which he was put in jail. A few months later, the United States Supreme Court ruled in his favour, declaring that Alabama's bus segregation laws were unconstitutional.

Rosa Parks became a symbol of the black struggle in the United States. After she died, her casket lay in state in the Capitol in Washington, an honour typically reserved for presidents of the United States.

now... Did you know... Did you know...

As a result of the black struggle, the American government passed two important laws: the Civil Rights Act (1964) and the Voting Rights Act (1965).

The Civil Rights Act	The Voting Rights Act
• This act recognized the equality of blacks and whites. • It put an end to **segregation**, allowing blacks to frequent the same public places as whites (schools, workplaces, hotels, restaurants, movie theatres, etc.).	• This act recognized that all citizens had the right to vote, whatever their colour. • It banned the use of literacy tests as a condition for voting, as these tests were often designed to disqualify blacks.

Although **racism** is not as prevalent as before, it still exists. But since obtaining these rights, black Americans have become mayors, senators, secretaries of state, etc. There has even been a black major-party nominee for president. Other blacks have become prominent in music, movies, sports and many other areas.

6.10 *Black American athletes Tommie Smith and John Carlos at the Olympic Games in Mexico City in 1968.*

When these two black athletes won gold and bronze medals, they turned their backs on the American flag and gave the raised-fist salute when the national anthem was played. This act of dissidence, aimed at criticizing racial segregation in their country, caused a frenzy in the United States and around the world.

segregation: the act of separating one group from the rest, usually as a form of discrimination.

racism: discrimination or prejudice based on race.

I agree. beacuase the American athletes were upset with their country for treating them like garbage.

Let's Get to Work!

1 Name two measures taken by the United States before the 20th century recognizing the rights of blacks.

- _Abolish ~~So~~ Slavery ,_

- _Constitution_

2 What evidence is there that blacks and whites were unequal in the United States in the mid-20th century? Write down three examples.

- _segregation of whites and blacks, whites and black couldn't get married, go the same school._
- _Blacks got paid less than whites._

- _Less opportunity._

3 How do you think blacks' participation in the Second World War influenced them to form a rights movement?

If Blacks fought for America, the lest America could do, is treat them with respect and equality.

4 Name three rights that Martin Luther King demanded for black Americans.

- _The right to vote,_
- _hight quality Jobs._
- _Equality with whites_

5 Which of the following acts of dissidence are nonviolent?

- ☑ Going on a hunger strike (fasting)
- ◯ Overturning police cars
- ◯ Throwing rocks at Parliament
- ☑ Demonstrating in the streets with placards
- ☑ Sitting in the restricted section of a bus
- ☑ Refusing to pay a fine
- ◯ Carrying out a suicide bombing
- ☑ Boycotting a business
- ☑ Writing a song denouncing the arrest of an activist

6 Indicate which law, the Civil Rights Act or the Voting Rights Act, gave blacks the following rights:

	CIVIL RIGHTS ACT	VOTING RIGHTS ACT
a) The right to go to the same stores as whites	✓	○
b) The right to vote in elections	○	✓
c) The right not to have to submit to literacy tests to be able to vote	○	✓
d) The right to go to the same schools as whites	✓	○
e) The right to go to the same movie theatres as whites	✓	○

7 Why do you think a literacy test might disqualify a black person from voting?

Because most Black people did not learn to read and write.

8 Put the following events in chronological order.

2	There was a boycott of the bus company.
1	Rosa Parks refused to give up her seat on the bus to a white person.
3	The United States Supreme Court declared the Alabama bus segregation laws unconstitutional.
4	Martin Luther King was awarded the Nobel Peace Prize.

9 Look at figure 6.10, on page 189.

a) Why do you think athletes Tommie Smith and John Carlos made this gesture of defiance, instead of celebrating their Olympic victory?

Because Blacks were upset with their country for treating them like garbage.

b) How do you think black Americans reacted to this act of dissidence?

The felt proud

c) How do you think white Americans felt when they saw this act of dissidence, which took place in front of the whole world? Check one answer.

○ Pride ✓ Shame ○ Relief

d) Was this act of dissidence violent or nonviolent?

Non violent.

The anti-apartheid movement in South Africa

反种族隔离运动

Once a colony of the Netherlands, and then of the United Kingdom, South Africa gained its independence in 1931. While its political system was democratic, nonwhites were excluded.

✦ In 1948, a white minority party came to power, as nonwhites did not have the right to vote. The National Party sought to strengthen the apartheid system, which was based on racial segregation. It passed segregationist laws such as the Population Registration Act and the Group Area Act.

Population Registration Act	Group Area Act
This act classified people into racial groups: white, black, coloured and Indian. All residents had to have identity cards specifying their race.	This act excluded nonwhites from the neighbourhoods where whites lived. It instituted separate schools, hospitals, beaches, buses and other public places, based on race.

Research Mandate

Do some research on a person who struggled against apartheid in South Africa, such as Nelson Mandela, Steve Biko, Desmond Tutu or Walter Sisulu.

In the 1970s, riots broke out in black neighbourhoods. They were violently repressed by police, and hundreds of demonstrators were killed. From this time on, international public opinion began to push governments into putting pressure on South Africa to end apartheid.

The mobilization of world public opinion brought results. Bowing to international pressure, President Frederik De Klerk abolished the apartheid system in 1991. Over a period of several years, he negotiated a new constitution with all of South Africa's ethnic groups. Nelson Mandela, who was elected president under the new constitution, appointed Frederik De Klerk as his vice-president, demonstrating that it was possible for a white and a black to lead South Africa together.

✦ "ASIMBONANGA"

British musician and singer Johnny Clegg lived in South Africa during his adolescence. Along with Zulu friends (the Zulus are a black South African people), he formed a group whose music combined African melodies with rock. His song "Asimbonanga" ("We have not seen him"), written in 1987, paid tribute to Nelson Mandela, who was still in prison at the time. It was censored by the South African government.

De Klerk and Mandela receiving the Nobel Peace Prize in 1993.

✦ NELSON MANDELA (BORN 1918)

A lawyer and a member of the African National Congress (ANC), Nelson Mandela organized a campaign against the South African government, and helped draw up the Freedom Charter for black South Africans. In the 1960s, he was sentenced to life imprisonment for his political activities.

In 1990, after 27 years behind bars, he was freed by the white president, Frederik De Klerk. Mandela and De Klerk together were awarded the Nobel Peace Prize in 1993. In 1994, Mandela was elected president of South Africa in the first multiracial election following the abolition of apartheid. He retired from South African politics in 1999. Since then, he has devoted himself to the struggle against AIDS, from which his son died in 2005 (the cover of this textbook shows Mandela at a benefit concert for his AIDS foundation).

---

apartheid: Afrikaans word meaning "separation" (Afrikaans is a language spoken by white South Africans).

censor: to ban a newspaper, book, song, film, etc., or parts of one, because of the ideas it expresses.

Let's Get to Work!

1 In 1945, South Africa's population was made up of many ethnic groups.

Blacks: 72% (including Zulus)

Whites: 16% (Afrikaners of Dutch descent, and British)

Coloureds: 9% (descendants of marriages between Europeans and blacks)

Indians: 3% (immigrants from India during the colonial period)

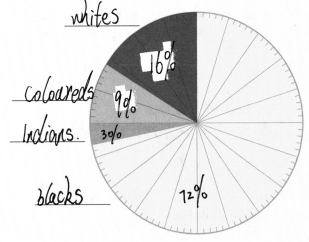

whites

coloureds 9%

Indians. 3%

16%

blacks

72%

a) Complete this chart by writing in the ethnic group corresponding to each segment.

b) Highlight in green the name of the group or groups that had the right to participate in public life in South Africa under apartheid. *whites.*

c) What does the chart say to you about public life in South Africa under apartheid?

It was very unfair and did not consider the needs of the majority of the population

2 Why couldn't Nelson Mandela be elected president of South Africa under apartheid?

Because he was Black

3 Governments sometimes use censorship to prevent a work (book, film, song, etc.) from being distributed.

a) Why was the song "Asimbonanga" censored in South Africa in the 1980s?

Because It was a tribute to nelson mandela who was in Jail.

b) Have you ever heard of a case of censorship? If so, why was it imposed?

Yes, songs on the radio with bad words get censored.

4 Name at least three ways in which people resisted apartheid in South Africa.

- *international pressure by groverments and olympics*
- *Boycott businesses loans had to be paid back Protests,*
- *marches etc.*

How Did the Feminist Movement Arise? 女权运动是如何兴起的?

At one time, women did not have the same rights as men. They did not have the right to vote or to be elected to public office, for example. <u>In the mid-19th century, women began to demand equal rights with men.</u> This movement is known as <u>feminism</u>.

The situation of women in the early 20th century 20世纪初期妇女的状况

In Western societies in the early 20th century, the role of women consisted of childrearing and housekeeping. Few women pursued higher education, as most universities did not admit them. Many professions, such as law and medicine, completely excluded women and were strictly reserved for men.

 Is there still inequality between men and women in Western societies?

Women were also considered unsuited to public life, as can be seen in this passage from an article by the French-Canadian journalist Henri Bourassa, founder of the Montreal daily *Le Devoir*.

> "The so-called 'right' to suffrage is just a reflection of the functions, or the social burdens that fall upon the shoulders of men, because of their mental and physical makeup, and especially because of their status and duties as head of the family. Women's main role is, and will remain, ... motherhood, the sacred role of fertility, which makes women equal to men – indeed, in many ways their superior. But motherhood inevitably must rule out responsiblities that are too heavy: military service, for example, or the civil service."
>
> Henri Bourassa, "Le droit de voter. La lutte des sexes. Laisserons-nous avilir nos femmes?" (The Right to Vote, the Battle of the Sexes: Shall We Allow Our Women to Be Dishonoured?), *Le Devoir*, March 30, 1918. Free translation.

The right to vote 投票权

The movement to win the right to vote began in Great Britain in 1865. These first feminist activists were known as suffragettes. The suffragettes used

dramatic gestures to win recognition of women's right to vote:
– they disrupted political meetings;
– they organized marches;
– they vandalized symbols of masculinity such as golf courses, which were reserved for men at the time.

6.11 *Suffragette demonstration in England in 1908.*

In 1914, the First World War broke out. With the men away at war, women worked in the weapons factories. It was the women who kept their countries' economies afloat. After the war, many governments recognized women's contribution to the war effort by granting them the right to vote. In France and Quebec, however, women were denied the right to vote until the Second World War.

Women's right to vote 妇女的选举权
1902: Australia 澳
1917: Canada
1918: Great Britain (for women over 30)
1920: United States
1928: Great Britain (for women over 21)
1940: Quebec
1944: France

suffrage: synonym for voting.

The feminist movement in Canada

In Canada, the feminist movement began in the early 20th century and is still active today. These are some of its pioneers.

 Marie Gérin-Lajoie (1867 to 1945)

 Marie Gérin-Lajoie, born Marie Lacoste, worked for the equality of men and women before the law and for the right to vote in Quebec. She ran up against the opposition of the Catholic Church, which was reluctant to agree to a broader role for women in society.

 Simonne Monet-Chartrand (1919 to 1993)

 Simonne Monet, the daughter of a judge and the wife of trade union leader Michel Chartrand, began her career as an activist at the age of 20, when she realized that she could not vote because she was a woman. In spite of having seven children, she remained an active feminist throughout her life. She participated in the founding of the Fédération des Femmes du Québec (Quebec women's federation) in 1966. She fought for the right to birth control at a time when it was forbidden by the church. She was also a peace activist and was involved in Quebec's Civil Liberties Union, an organization for the defence of the rights recognized in international charters.

Claire Kirkland-Casgrain (1924)

 In 1961, Claire Kirkland-Casgrain became the first woman elected to the Quebec legislature. She was also Quebec's first woman cabinet minister. In 1964, under her leadership, the Quebec legislature passed a law recognizing the legal capacity of married women. This allowed a married woman to buy property or borrow money from the bank without her husband's consent.

Research Mandate

Do some research about another Quebec feminist activist, such as Idola St-Jean, Thérèse Casgrain or Elizabeth Monk.

In addition to the right to vote, the feminist movement has struggled for better access for women to education and jobs.

Since 1966, the Fédération des Femmes du Québec has worked for the interests of women in Quebec. Today, the Fédération promotes better representation for women in politics, and works to end the violence and poverty of which many women are victims.

Some gains that women have made in Canada

1903: Irma Levasseur, first woman medical specialist in Quebec (she had completed her degree in the United States)

1904: Marie Sirois, first woman to graduate from a French-language university (Laval)

1920: Agnes MacPhail, first woman elected to the Canadian Parliament

1929: Elsie Gregory MacGill, first woman engineer in Canada

1946: Jeanne d'Arc Lemay-Warren, first woman admitted to the Quebec bar to practise as a lawyer

1961: Claire Kirkland-Casgrain, first woman elected to the Quebec legislature

1962: Claire Kirkland-Casgrain, first woman cabinet minister in Quebec

1984: Jeanne Sauvé, first woman governor general of Canada

1993: Kim Campbell, first woman prime minister of Canada

2000: Beverley McLachlin, first woman chief justice of the Supreme Court of Canada

---

Despite this progress, there is still a long way to go. For example, in 1996 the Quebec National Assembly adopted the Pay Equity Act, which requires employers to give women the same pay as men for equivalent tasks. It is still difficult to implement this legislation in 2008.

Let's Get to Work!

1 Name at least three forms of discrimination against women in the early 20th century.

- Women didn't have the right to vote.
- Couldn't go to University.
- many jobs were only for men.

2 In politics, a point of view can be progressive or conservative.

a) Look up the meaning of these two words in a dictionary.

1. Progressive: To think progress and moving forward

2. Conservative: Keep things as is. Do Not Change!!!

b) In terms of women's role in society, would you say that Canadian society in the early 20th century was progressive or conservative? Give reasons for your answer.

Conservative. Canadians initially did not want women to vote.

3 Reread the passage from the article by Henri Bourassa on page 194.

a) According to Henri Bourassa,

1. what is the main role of women in society? Motherhood (baby machine)

2. what roles should be reserved for men only? Military and civil service

b) On the basis of this passage, would you say that Henri Bourassa's point of view on the role of women was progressive or conservative? Give reasons for your answer.

Conservative. He did not want women's ~~role~~ role to change.

4 a) Give at least two examples of acts of dissidence carried out by suffragettes in the 19th century.

- Vandalized, hunger strikes, organized marches, disrupted
- meetings etc...

b) In general, do these acts seem to you to be violent or peaceful?

peaceful

5 What international event contributed to women's winning the right to vote?

WW1

6 How do you think giving women the right to vote helped bring about a more democratic society?

More people get to vote.

7 a) In Canada, how much time passed between

1. the election of the first woman to Parliament and the appointment of the first woman prime minister?

   13 years

2. the admission of the first woman lawyer to the Quebec bar and the appointment of the first woman chief justice of the Supreme Court?

   54 years

b) On the basis of your answers to part a), comment on the pace at which attitudes change.

   slow

8 How did the situation of women in Quebec improve during the 20th century? Name at least three improvements.

- _right to vote_
- _right to go to university_
- _right to get a loan_

9 What are the current demands of the Fédération des Femmes du Québec?

end poverty and violence towards women

10 Fill out the crossword below using the definitions given.

1. Institution that resisted feminism
2. Movement that promotes the rights of women
3. Right that was demanded by feminists
4. Name given to British feminists in the 19th century
5. First country to give women the right to vote
6. Profession that used to be closed to women

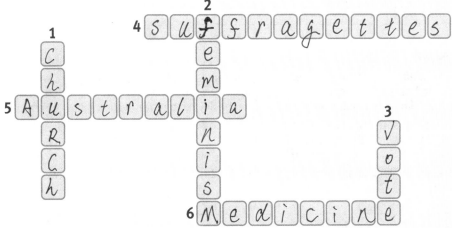

What Was the Situation of Jews in the 20th Century?

20世纪的犹太人 情况如何.

The rights of several groups were recognized in the 20th century, including colonized peoples, blacks and women. On the other hand, extremist groups in the 20th century deprived some people of the most basic human rights, including the right to life. For example, European Jews were victims of a racist political system, before and during the Second World War.

6.12 GERMANY IN SEPTEMBER 1939

🕉 Auschwitz concentration camp

0   580 km

Anti-Semitism in the early 20th century

20世纪初的 反犹主义.

Millions of Jews lived in Europe in the early 20th century. The Jews were a religious minority in many countries, including Germany and Poland. They were often victims of discrimination because of their religion. Discrimination against Jews is called anti-Semitism.

Adolf Hitler and the Nazi Party

As you saw on page 179, Germany lost territory at the end of the First World War and had to pay heavy reparations to the Allies. During the Great Depression of the 1930s, Germans lived in misery and felt humiliated.

It was at this point that Adolf Hitler came on the political scene. Many Germans saw this party leader as a man who could restore the dignity of the German people. Hitler was the leader of the National Socialist German Workers Party, or Nazi Party, whose symbol was the swastika. Taking advantage of the weaknesses of Germany's democratic system, Hitler took power in 1933 and retained it until the end of the Second World War. During those years, Germany adopted an officially racist political system.

✵ MEIN KAMPF

Adolf Hitler wrote *Mein Kampf* (My Struggle) in 1925. In it he laid out his political ideology, which became the ideology of the Nazi party. Among other things, he <u>criticized</u> the way Europe was divided up at the Treaty of Versailles, and claimed that Polish, Austrian and Czechoslovakian territory should be part of Germany.

Hitler was convinced that the German race was superior to others, and that Germany's duty was to rid Europe of "inferior" races that were harming civilization, such as the Jews. He feared that the purity of the German race would be lost through the mixing of the "inferior" and "superior" races.

The ideas expressed in Mein Kampf were communicated to the people through the Nazis' vast **propaganda** network.

---

propaganda: distribution of information aimed at convincing the public to accept particular ideas.

The Nuremberg Laws

✳ As soon as they took power, Nazis began to encourage Germans to boycott businesses owned by Jews. In 1935, in the city of Nuremberg, they passed anti-Jewish laws, carrying their racist policy a step further:

– Jews were stripped of their German citizenship;
– Jews no longer had political rights;
– marriages between Jews and non-Jews were banned to protect "the purity of German blood."

Other laws passed in the early years of Nazi rule deprived Jews of the right to practise some professions, such as medicine, teaching and the civil service.

Many Jews left Germany after these laws were passed. Soon afterwards, the Nazis went even further:

– Jews had to identify themselves clearly by wearing a yellow star;
– their property was confiscated.

It was in this context that the Second World War broke out between Germany and the Allies.

✳ **6.13** *The Auschwitz concentration camp.*
Auschwitz-Birkenau, in Poland, was the largest concentration and extermination camp ever built. More than a million people, most of them Jews, died there.

The Holocaust

The **genocide** of the Jews during the Second World War is known as the Holocaust. In 1942, in the Berlin suburb of Wannsee, leading figures in the Nazi party decided to organize what they called the "final solution to the Jewish problem," which consisted of the elimination, pure and simple, of all the Jews in Europe.

✳ "Under proper guidance, in the course of the final solution the Jews are to be allocated for appropriate labour in the East. Able-bodied Jews, separated according to sex, will be taken in large work columns to these areas for work on roads, in the course of which action doubtless a large portion will be eliminated by natural causes ... In the course of the practical execution of the final solution, Europe will be combed through from west to east ... The evacuated Jews will first be sent, group by group, to so-called transit ghettos, from which they will be transported to the East."

Excerpt from the *Wannsee Protocol*, January 20, 1942.

> What other genocides or crimes against humanity have you heard of?

The Nazis organized concentration and extermination camps in Poland, and later in other parts of Europe.

Nazi policies brought about the death of between 5 million and 6 million Jews, representing more than half the Jews in Europe at the time. Other groups, such as Roma, the mentally challenged, gays and blacks, were also targets of Nazi extermination policies.

> Compare the number of Jews killed with the total population of Quebec. What do you notice?

---

political right: the right to participate in public life.
genocide: deliberate destruction of an ethnic or religious group.

ghetto: place where Jews were confined.
Roma: Gypsies.

In 1945, the Germans were defeated and Hitler committed suicide in Berlin. After the war, the Allies organized a special tribunal in Nuremberg, the city where the anti-Jewish laws had been proclaimed, to bring the leading Nazis to trial. Twelve of the Nazi leaders were sentenced to death and seven others were sent to prison.

✷ Individuals who opposed Nazi policies, such as the factory owner Oskar Schindler, helped some Jews escape death. Schindler saved hundreds of Jews from the Holocaust by having them work in his factories. Steven Spielberg's film *Schindler's List* tells his story.

✷ ANNE FRANK'S DIARY

Anne Frank (1929 to 1945) was a young German Jew. When Hitler took power, her family fled Germany and settled in the Netherlands. In 1940, Germany invaded the Netherlands and the Frank family had to hide. In 1944, the Gestapo (the Nazi secret police) found their hiding place. The family was sent to a concentration camp and Anne Frank died there at the age of 16, two months before the camp was liberated by the Allies.

Anne's father, who survived Auschwitz, had his daughter's diary published. In her diary, Anne described daily life in the hiding place where she had had to spend several years. The diary of Anne Frank has been translated into more than 60 languages.

"I can't tell you how oppressive it is never to be able to go outdoors, also I'm scared to death that we shall be discovered and be shot. This is not exactly a pleasant prospect. We have to whisper and tread lightly during the day, otherwise, the people in the warehouse might hear us."

The Diary of Anne Frank, translated from the Dutch by B.M. Mooyart-Doubleday. London: Pan Books, 1954.

Let's Get to Work!

1 Give two reasons why Germans were frustrated in the 1930s.

• *Germany lost territory, had to pay heavy reparations ($)*

• *they were also humiliated for losing the war.*

2 Which of the following ideologies was the one that made Hitler popular in Germany? Check the correct answer.

◯ Pacifism

◯ Liberalism

☑ Nationalism

◯ Democracy

3 Many documents give us information about Nazi policies in the 1930s and 1940s.
Match each document with the information found in it.

a) Document proving that the genocide of the Jews was planned and organized. **2**

b) Propaganda document stating that Jews were inferior to other Germans. **4**

c) Document that withdrew Jews' political rights and forbade them to marry non-Jews. **3**

d) Document that describes the daily life of Jews who were in hiding during the Nazi regime. **1**

1. Anne Frank's diary

2. The report of the Wannsee Conference

3. The Nuremberg Laws

4. Adolf Hitler's book *Mein Kampf*

4 Locate these events on the timeline below.

a) Nuremberg Laws **1935**
b) Start of Second World War **1939**
c) Publication of *Mein Kampf* **1925**
d) Hitler's accession to power **1933**
e) End of Second World War **1945**
f) Nuremberg Trials **1945**
g) Wannsee Conference **1942**

c, d, a, b, g, e, f.

Don't forget to mark years on the timeline.

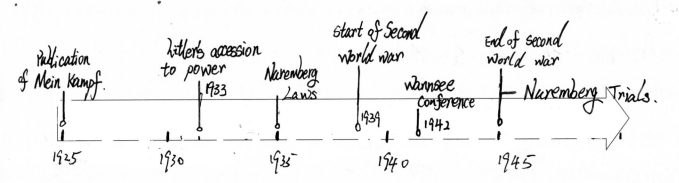

5 After the Second World War, the Allies rebuilt Germany.
Why do you think they did this?

They helped Germany because they didn't want them to start another world war.

6 Match each term on the left with its definition.

a) Holocaust   _3_   1. Premeditated elimination of an ethnic or religious group

b) Genocide   _1_   2. Germany's political system from 1933 to 1945

c) Propaganda   _5_   3. Extermination of millions of Jews in Europe

d) Anti-Semitism   _4_   4. Hatred of Jews

e) Nazism   _2_   5. Distribution of information to influence public opinion

7 Other than the Jews, name two groups that the Germans persecuted on the pretext that they were "inferior."

- _blacks, disabled, gays, gypsies_
- _____

8 Propaganda is sometimes used to persuade people to accept an idea. Propaganda often distorts reality. How can you be sure that something you hear or read is correct information and not propaganda?

Today we have access to a lot of information (internet, books) so the best way to find out is by doing your own research.

9 Indicate whether the following statements are true or false. If a statement is false, write the correct version underneath.

                                                  TRUE   FALSE

a) The genocide of the Jews was not planned. .... ○ .... ✓

It was planned

b) About 25% of European Jews lost their lives under the Nazi regime. .... ○ .... ✓

More than 25%

c) Only Jews were targeted by the Nazi government's racist policies. .... ○ .... ✓

There were many others

d) The Germans won the Second World War. .... ○ .... ✓

They lost

10 Name three activities that you participate in that Anne Frank couldn't do because she had to be in hiding.

_____

_____

_____

Let's Get to Work!

Synthesis Activities

1 Which of the following measures were used in the 20th century to deprive groups of their rights? Check the right answers.

○ Censorship   ○ Imprisonment

○ Repression   ○ Genocide

2 Using arrows, match each of the following concepts to the right it corresponds to.

a) Decolonization

Right of peoples to self-determination

b) Anti-racism

Right to equality

c) Feminism

3 Using the following definitions, fill in the acrostic below to find the name of a passionate defender of the rights of black South Africans.

1. Title of a song censored by the South African government
2. Majority deprived of their rights under the apartheid system in South Africa
3. International prize awarded to an outstanding person
4. Synonym for disobedience
5. To ban a work (book, film, etc.) because of the ideas it expresses
6. Describes rights of individuals recognized in a charter or law
7. Separation of whites and nonwhites in South Africa

4 One of the words in each of the series below doesn't belong. Circle the intruder, and explain why it doesn't belong.

a) France, United Kingdom, United States, Germany, USSR

_____

_____

b) Suffragettes, Rosa Parks, pay equity, Fédération des Femmes du Québec

_____

_____

c) Hitler, Nazi, swastika, Nuremberg Laws, Ku Klux Klan

_____

_____

(5) Fill in the index cards below, using what you have learned in this Inquiry.

Name: _____

Profession: _____

What goal did he work for? _____

_____

What did he do to reach his goal? _____

_____

_____

Was he involved in politics? If so, in which party? _____

Was he put in jail? _____

Name: _____

Profession: _____

What goal did he work for? _____

_____

What did he do to reach his goal? _____

_____

_____

Was he involved in politics? If so, in which party? _____

Was he put in jail? _____

Name: _____

Profession: _____

What goal did he work for? _____

_____

What did he do to reach his goal? _____

_____

_____

Was he involved in politics? If so, in which party? _____

Was he put in jail? _____

Synthesis Activities

Name: _____

Profession: _____

What goal did he work for? _____

_____

What did he do to reach his goal? _____

_____

_____

Was he involved in politics? If so, in which party? _____

Was he put in jail? _____

6) Using the index cards you filled in above, answer the following questions.

a) What profession did Mohandas Gandhi, Habib Bourguiba and Nelson Mandela all practise?

_____

b) What is the connection between this profession and working for rights?

_____

_____

c) What is the connection between Martin Luther King's profession and working for rights?

_____

_____

7) Is it necessary to practise a prestigious profession to be able to advance a social cause? Use an example from this Inquiry to support your answer.

_____

_____

_____

8) a) Name a freedom or right that is not respected in the world.

_____

_____

_____

_____

b) What could you do to become involved in promoting respect for that freedom or right?

_____

_____

_____

Inquiry Conclusion

SUMMARIZE WHAT YOU HAVE LEARNED

Use the following words to write a short text explaining how the movement to win civil rights and freedoms developed.

> discrimination • feminism • racism • right • colony • dissidence •
> equality • right to vote • blacks • self-determination

_____

_____

_____

_____

_____

_____

_____

_____

_____

RETURN TO THE SECTION "ON THE TRAIL"

Return to pages 176 and 177 and reread your responses to the questions asked. Reassess them in the light of what you have learned since. Then try to answer the two questions that you wrote down on page 177. If you cannot, try to figure out why.

Discuss and Take a Stand

Even if individual rights are written into laws and charters, and discrimination and segregation are illegal, there are times in our daily lives when we deny these rights to others. For example, you may have kept a student out of your group, prevented a student from sitting where he or she wished in the cafeteria, repeatedly made fun of a student who spoke in class, etc. All these behaviours that exclude people, whatever the reasons behind them, are examples of discrimination.

Respect for rights is the responsibility of all members of society, no matter how young. What concrete action do you think you could take so that there would no longer be discrimination in your milieu?

[TC] Your teacher will give you a worksheet including questions and illustrations as clues. Try to answer the questions using the visual clues. Then discuss your answers with your classmates.

Inquiry 7 Globalization: A Social Phenomenon of the Present

On the Trail

Studying societies of the past has helped you to discover their many legacies, or what they have contributed to societies of today. While present-day societies may differ from one another in terms of their wealth, political systems, culture and religion, the economic ties that link them are becoming closer and closer.

Look at the illustrations on these two pages and then answer the questions.

7.1 In the Neolithic period, trade took the form of barter.

7.2 Nowadays people can shop on the Internet.

7.3 Many consumer goods enter Canada through the Port of Montreal.

How has trade changed since the days of barter?

_____

_____

_____

_____

_____

Where do the consumer goods you own come from?

_____

_____

_____

_____

_____

At a Glance

What Was the Context of the Growth of Globalization?

Globalization can be defined as the expansion of trade to a worldwide scale. Today, few countries can escape its influence, whether for good or for ill.

The origins of globalization

Globalization is a complex phenomenon. It affects many areas of society, including the economy, health, culture and politics.

For example,

– European countries have created a common currency, the euro, to make trade easier;

– researchers worldwide share medical breakthroughs;

– groups of musicians use the Internet to become known throughout the world;

– governments create international organizations to maintain peace or establish rules for doing business.

With globalization, countries have become economically interdependent, and none are completely closed to the outside world. Not every country, however, participates in world trade on an equal footing, as the map below shows.

The globalization of trade is not a new phenomenon, as you have learned through your studies. The difference now is that it affects almost every country in the world. The following pages will remind you of some of the landmarks in the history of globalization.

7.4 COUNTRIES' PARTICIPATION IN GLOBAL TRADE

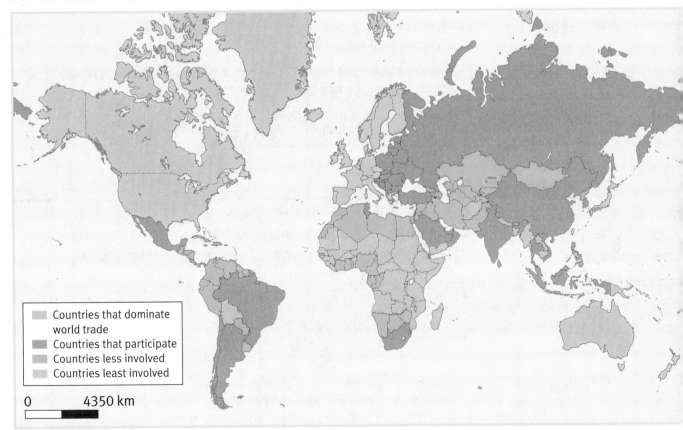

Legend:
- Countries that dominate world trade
- Countries that participate
- Countries less involved
- Countries least involved

0   4350 km

Evolution of trade

Neolithic	• Division of labour, first sign of various trades (artisans, traders, etc.)
Antiquity	• Invention of the wheel, merchant shipping, Roman roads • Use of slave labour in Mesopotamia, Athens and the Roman Empire • Invention of metal coins • Trade between Europe and Asia along the Silk Road
Middle Ages	• Many trade cities • Trading between Europe and Africa through Arab merchants • Invention of the bill of exchange (banknotes and cheques) • Merchant associations (hanses and guilds) regulating trade
Modern Times	• Beginning of trade on a global scale ("world economy")
Contemporary Era	• Mechanization → increased production • Invention of new methods of transportation (locomotives, steamships, cars, airplanes, etc.) → increase in trade • World economic crises (Great Depression in the 1930s, for example)

Evolution of health

Neolithic	• Agriculture → better nutrition → population increase
Antiquity	• Crop rotation → improvements in agriculture • Initial contact between peoples → wars and epidemics
Middle Ages	• Advances in agriculture (new tools) → population increase • Epidemics, such as bubonic plague
Modern Times	• European discovery of America → deaths of millions of indigenous people through measles, smallpox, bubonic plague, etc.
Contemporary Era	• Advances in agriculture and public health → population increase • Pollution by factories → high death rate among workers

Evolution of cultural exchange

Neolithic	• Statuettes of mother-goddesses found in scattered locations
Antiquity	• Invention of writing → communication over greater distances • Spread of Roman culture throughout the Roman Empire (Latin language, polytheistic religion followed by Christianity, architecture and recreation)
Middle Ages	• Spread of Christianity and Islam via trade cities
Modern Times	• Spread of Italian art throughout Europe during the Renaissance • Invention of printing press → spread of humanist ideas throughout Europe • Spread of European cultures to Africa and Asia through evangelization
Contemporary Era	• Spread of Enlightenment ideas throughout Europe • Spread of European languages in Africa

Evolution of political structures

Neolithic	• Organization into villages
Antiquity	• City-states, then kingdoms and empires • First democracy in Athens (equality of citizens) • Authoritarian political regimes (monarchies, oligarchies, etc.) • Code of Hammurabi: one of the earliest written codes of law • Interest in keeping peace throughout the Roman Empire
Middle Ages	• Europe divided into kingdoms (hereditary monarchies)
Modern Times	• Colonial empires (mother countries and colonies) established
Contemporary Era	• English, American and French revolutions: spread of democracy • Rights (equality, vote) and freedoms (of religion, thought, the press) • Economic liberalism (no state intervention in the economy) • Socialism (labour laws) • Decolonization of America, then of Africa and Asia • Struggle for equal rights (women, blacks, etc.) • Creation of the UN to prevent conflicts

Supporters and critics

While some believe globalization is both desirable and profitable, others believe that, in its current form, globalization is not contributing to human progress. This debate can be seen as today's version of the 19th-century argument between supporters of economic liberalism and supporters of socialism.

Supporters of globalization	Critics of globalization

• Supporters of economic neoliberalism argue that market competition alone is enough to regulate world trade relations.
 	
• Entrepreneurs who run multinational corporations, and rich countries in general, are in favour of globalization, as it enables them to increase trade and become wealthy.
	• Critics of globalization point out that globalization today is widening the gap between rich and poor people. They advocate restrictions on international trade.
	
	• This position is supported by a wide variety of groups in both rich and poor countries, for example,
	  – protesters who take dramatic action
	  – newspapers and magazines, such as *This Magazine*
	  – associations such as the environmental group Greenpeace and many trade unions.

7.5 *Brian Mulroney, then Prime Minister of Canada, signing the North American Free Trade Agreement (NAFTA) with the United States and Mexico in 1992.*

7.6 *Student march protesting against the Free Trade Area of the Americas (FTAA).*

economic neoliberalism: an ideology that opposes any restrictions on the global free market.

Let's Get to Work!

1 Compare map 7.4, on page 209, with map 5.1, on page 140. What link can you see between a country's participation in world trade and its level of development?

....

....

2 Indicate which of the following statements show continuity with the past and which show a change from societies of the past.

		CONTINUITY	CHANGE
a)	Use of written communication	○	○
b)	Trading across large distances	○	○
c)	Use of metal and paper money	○	○
d)	Epidemics	○	○
e)	Artists becoming known throughout the world via television	○	○
f)	Very rapid communication due to digital technology	○	○
g)	Agricultural advances leading to better nutrition	○	○
h)	Use of electronic money and credit cards	○	○
i)	Rapid advances in medicine	○	○

3 Imagine you were the following people. Would you be more likely to be for or against globalization?

a) I am an American filmmaker, and I want my film to be seen all over the world.

....

b) I am a Canadian filmmaker, and I'm having trouble distributing my film as all the movie theatres belong to American companies.

....

c) I'm a farmer, and I'm afraid my competitors in other countries will force me to lower my prices.

....

d) I raise cattle, and my main customers are the Americans and the Japanese.

....

e) I'm an ordinary consumer, and I just want to pay the lowest price possible for the things I buy, wherever they come from.

....

f) I'm an ordinary consumer, and I like trying exotic new products.

....

g) I'm a student, and my father just lost his job in a factory because of Asian competition.

....

Project

Globalization is at the heart of most of the great social issues of our time. Its effects are felt in many areas, as you will discover in the following pages. Some of its impacts are positive, others not. Everywhere on the planet there are some people who support unrestricted globalization, while others want to set limits on it.

Task: In this last Inquiry, we invite you to deepen your knowledge of globalization and its origins so that you can take a stand in a classroom debate. The debate will centre around this question: Does globalization unite people, or does it create inequalities between people?

Final product required: A complete research file on one area of globalization that will enable you to take part in a debate, using relevant arguments.

Several steps are necessary to complete the project.

1 Read the five dossiers in this Inquiry and then complete the activities suggested.

2 Choose one of the five dossiers.

3 Ask at least three questions about the dossier covering the area you chose. Your questions must lead you to a deeper understanding of that area. For example,
- Dossier on the economies of rich countries: What are the main free trade agreements currently in effect?
- Dossier on the economies of poor countries: In a globalized world, how can poor countries overcome poverty?
- Dossier on health and the environment: When and how did we start to be concerned about the effects of pollution?
- Dossier on culture: Who is against cultural globalization, and why?
- Dossier on politics: Are interventions by the International Monetary Fund (IMF) always useful to the countries receiving their aid?

Using the following format, write down your questions on a sheet, and add it to your research file.

Chosen dossier:
Questions on the dossier
Question 1:
Question 2:
Question 3:

4 Following the format below, demonstrate how your chosen area of globalization has changed since Neolithic times by

a) writing down which historical situations influenced the development of globalization in your chosen area; naming the period in which they occured and describing them as accurately as possible;

b) drawing a timeline and locating these historical situations on your timeline in chronological order;

c) commenting on which aspects of society show continuity, and which show change.

You can look at pages 210 and 211 to give you ideas. To complete your sheet, add other information that you've learned since starting high school. You can also do extra research. Use all the resources you can find. Your teacher can help you at this stage of the project by suggesting research avenues.

Add the sheet to your research kit.

Evolution of chosen area of globalization
Historical situation: *Historical situation 1: When? What? Where? Who? How?* *Historical situation 2: When? What? Where? Who? How?* *Etc.*
Timeline:
Elements that continued: *Describe the situations that have not changed over time*
Elements that changed: *Describe the situations that have changed over time and explain in what way they have changed*

5 Now come up with some arguments for and against globalization in the area that you chose. Write down your arguments on a new sheet, using the format on the next page, and specify who might put forward such an argument. Then write down why these people, or this group of people, might take this position. Find information (statistics, for example) that support your arguments.

You can further your research by consulting books, magazines, the Internet and any other relevant sources. Don't forget to clearly identify the sources you consulted. Your teacher can give you worksheets to help you record all the information you collect. He or she can also help you in your research by directing you to relevant sources. Your information should be presented clearly and in sufficient detail.

Add this sheet to your research file.

Arguments for and against globalization	
Arguments for globalization	
Argument 1: *Explain the argument*	
Supporters of this point of view: *Name the people or groups*	
Why they support this point of view: *Explain the reasons*	
Sources of information: *Write down where you found your information*	
Arguments against globalization	
Argument 1:	
Supporters of this point of view:	
Why they support this point of view:	
Sources of information:	

6

In a text of 150 to 250 words, explain the challenge that globalization presents today in your chosen area. Your text should have three sections:

1. Introduction:
   - Indicate which area of globalization you have chosen to study.
   - Write a brief history of how this area of globalization has evolved.
2. Body of the text:
   - Introduce the key figures in this debate (people, institutions, organizations) and present their arguments.
   - Describe what action is currently being taken in support of or against globalization.
3. Conclusion:
   - Conclude with your own opinion on the original question: Does globalization unite people, or does it create inequalities between people?

Add this text to your research file.

7

In the light of what you have learned, decide if you are for or against globalization. Prepare your part in the debate by writing out each of your arguments on index cards.

8

Take part in the classroom debate on your chosen area of globalization, using the arguments you wrote down on your index cards.

9

Evaluate your own participation in the debate.

How Does Economic Globalization Affect Rich Countries?

As the exchange of goods and services has become globalized, international trade has expanded. How does this affect the workplace? Who controls this trade? Does economic globalization only benefit rich countries?

The international division of labour

With industrialization in the 19th century, each worker performed a single step in the production process. Economic globalization is now changing the way tasks are divided: each step in the process may now be performed in a different country, depending on where costs are lowest. Multinational companies are dividing up labour this way to increase their profits.

This diagram gives an example of the new international division of labour:

United States	The United States government gives subsidies to cotton producers, which bring down its price.
↓	
India	A multinational company buys raw cotton in the United States, has it made into cloth in India, then into clothes in Bangladesh – both countries where workers' wages are low.
↓	
Bangladesh	
↓	
United States and Canada	The clothes are then sold by the multinational to North American consumers in retail chain stores.

Free trade

Free trade is trade that takes place without protectionist barriers such as import quotas or customs duties. Supporters of economic globalization are in favour of free trade, which allows goods and services to travel around the world without restriction.

Through free trade, multinationals can increase their profits by selling their products to more people, and industrialized countries can increase their wealth. This is why the most industrialized countries in the world are the main supporters of globalization.

7.7 *Canadian multinational Bombardier sells its airplanes to many countries, including China.*

✴ THE WORLD TRADE ORGANIZATION (WTO)

The World Trade Organization was founded in 1994. It has about 150 member countries, including Canada. Its goal is to promote the free movement of goods and services around the world. Negotiations lead to trade agreements, which are then ratified by member countries. The WTO is also asked to settle trade disputes between countries.

---

multinational: a corporation that operates in many countries.
subsidy: government aid to a business.
import quota: maximum quantity of a product allowed to be imported.

customs duty: tax imposed on products that cross a border.
ratify: synonym for approve.

GLOBALIZATION AND RICH COUNTRIES

Advantages	Disadvantages
• Multinationals benefit because they can have goods produced in poor countries where wages are low. • Consumers in rich countries have a choice of a wide variety of commodities at low prices. • By reducing production costs, large corporations can pay high salaries, especially in marketing and administration. • About 80% of jobs in rich countries are in the service sector, where globalization has little impact.	• In sectors that require unskilled labour: – corporations move operations to countries where wages are low (the Canadian automobile industry moving production to Mexico, for example, or call centres for Canadian companies moving to India); – factories close (the closing of Canadian textile factories, for example, because of competition in Asia). Rich countries are thus losing jobs.

For rich countries, the advantages of globalization (low prices and overall wealth increase) far outweigh the disadvantages (job losses), which are limited to a few regions and a few economic sectors.

Let's Get to Work!

1 When there is a trade dispute between two countries, what organization plays the role of judge? Write out its name in full.

_____

2 a) Do consumers in rich countries benefit from economic globalization? Explain your answer.

_____

_____

b) Do multinationals benefit from economic globalization? Explain your answer.

_____

_____

_____

3 What is the overall impact of economic globalization in rich countries? Check the correct answer.

◯ For rich countries there are no disadvantages.

◯ For rich countries there are as many advantages as disadvantages.

◯ For rich countries there are more advantages than disadvantages.

How Does Economic Globalization Affect Poor Countries?

Africa and parts of Asia benefit very little, if at all, from economic globalization. Trade mostly takes place among rich countries and newly industrialized countries, which deliberately exclude poor countries from their free trade agreements. Why are poor countries not able to participate in world trade? What are the main obstacles facing them?

The problem of debt

In the 1960s and 1970s, poor countries borrowed money from rich countries. Democracy was weak in poor countries, and there was no control on spending. Poor countries currently owe about $2 trillion to rich countries and to multinational banks. These countries have trouble making the interest payments on their debts.

Nowadays, when there is a drop in the world market price of a poor country's principal export, it is a catastrophe for that country's economy. The country can no longer manage to pay back its debt. This is what happened in 1998 in Guatemala, Nicaragua and Burundi when the price of coffee fell.

> "In northern Nicaragua's Matagalpa region ... more than forty larger coffee farms have gone bankrupt or lie idle. An estimated 6,000 homeless coffee workers and their families camp in makeshift homes along roads and in municipal parks, begging for food and help from passersby ... In Burundi, coffee accounts for almost 80 per cent of total exports ... Without money from coffee, there are fewer funds for debt repayment, AIDS strategies or schools."
>
> Sarah Cox, "Coffee Crisis." *Alternatives*, 7:10, 2003.

Lack of investment

There are several reasons why economic development in poor countries is not an attractive investment opportunity for investors from rich countries:
– poor countries often have unstable, corrupt and undemocratic governments, or governments that are against foreign investment;
– respect for human rights (such as the right to private property) is not always guaranteed;
– health care is poor, and there is a low level of education, making the labour force less attractive to corporations.

Without investment, the poorest countries cannot develop new businesses and remain shut out of world trade.

However, some formerly underdeveloped countries, including Brazil, India, China, Korea, Taiwan, Thailand and the Philippines, have seen rapid economic growth. This is thanks to globalization, which has enabled their industries to develop. More trade has slightly reduced poverty in some of these countries, and a middle class has formed. Within these "emerging" countries, however, the new wealth is not evenly distributed.

Difficulties for agricultural countries

The economies of poor countries often depend on agriculture. These countries have trouble taking part in world trade because rich countries protect their own agriculture with subsidies. It is hard for African countries to sell their cotton, for example, because the United States government subsidizes its own cotton producers. Consumers then buy American cotton rather than African cotton, because the price is lower.

As a result, poor countries must focus their agricultural production on export crops that are not grown in rich countries, such as coffee, cocoa and sugar.

7.8 *Tea plantation in Sri Lanka, Asia. These women work for meagre wages.*

These crops are often grown on immense plantations owned by large corporations. Peasants abandon the cultivation of their own food staples, such as corn or beans, to work on these plantations. In 2003, at the World Trade Organization summit in Mexico, the poor countries insisted that rich countries change their agricultural policies and stop subsidizing their own producers. The rich countries refused, and negotiations were broken off.

> "Peru produces just over 3,000,000 tonnes of alpaca wool per year, 80% of which is exported. The wool is mostly produced on small-scale Andean farms. Other countries are now taking an interest in this market, however, including China, Australia, New Zealand, the United States and Canada. Australia, in particular, is investing substantially in research to improve livestock reproduction and wool quality ... This trend is endangering the livelihood of countless Andean families who have neither the means nor the technology to stay competitive."
>
> Simon Thibault, "Les oubliés des Andes" (The Forgotten Andeans), *L'Actualité*, May 15, 2005. Free translation.

Let's Get to Work!

1 Why did poor countries borrow money in the 1960s and 1970s?

_____

2 Write down three effects of a drop in income for a poor country.

- _____
- _____
- _____

3 Why don't you think companies want a workforce that is poorly educated and has inadequate health care?

_____

_____

_____

How Does Globalization Affect Health and the Environment?

Globalization was made possible by cheap and efficient means of transportation. What are the effects of these means of transportation on the environment? How does the migration of people from poor countries to rich countries affect health? What are the health effects of tourism on a world scale?

The spread of disease

Without being aware of it, travellers have always been carriers of infectious agents, especially viruses, that cause communicable diseases. Remember, for example, how the indigenous population was ravaged by disease when America was colonized. With globalized trade today, people are constantly moving from one continent to another (about 500 million people take airplanes every year), and this multiplies the chances of disease spreading. There are vaccines against some communicable diseases, such as tuberculosis or poliomyelitis, but not against others, including AIDS. The planet is in a state of high alert against the threat of pandemics.

On the other hand, it is thanks to globalization that scientists throughout the world are able to share their discoveries, which has led to rapid advances in medicine.

7.9 *Students wearing masks as a protection against Severe Acute Respiratory Syndrome (SARS) in China, 2003.*

pollution is caused by industry, consumers also bear some responsibility:
- they use polluting methods of transportation, such as cars, which emit greenhouse gases;
- they consume products that have travelled a great distance rather than consuming local products which consume far less fuel;
- they produce vast quantities of garbage, which contaminates soils at waste disposal sites.

As the effects of pollution are felt all over the planet, cooperation on a worldwide scale is needed to find a solution.

Did you know...

TUBERCULOSIS

Tuberculosis is a communicable disease that usually attacks the lungs. This fatal illness was catastrophic in the 19th century, because no one had a cure. The development of a vaccine and antibiotics in the 20th century almost entirely eliminated the disease from industrialized countries. Yet tuberculosis is still a real threat today, because there are millions of sufferers throughout the world, especially in poor countries.

Effects on the environment

The use of polluting, non-renewable energy sources such as coal or oil, along with an increase in consumer goods, has created problems for the environment: climate change, thinning of the ozone layer and garbage disposal. While most of the

> "A rise in temperature of just 2°C. That's all it took to melt the Wisconsin glacier, which covered the whole of North America 15,000 years ago. A glacier that was 2 kilometres thick! Yet since the preindustrial era (1750), the temperature of the planet has risen by 0.8%°C."
>
> Benoît Aubin, "Les aventuriers du climat perdu" (Explorers of the Lost Climate). *L'Actualité*, October 15, 2005. Free translation.

pandemic: an epidemic that spreads over a very large area.

✵ THE KYOTO PROTOCOL

In 1997, representatives of countries all over the world met in Kyoto, Japan, to draw up a plan for reducing the greenhouse gases that are causing global warming.

The goal of the Kyoto Protocol was to reduce greenhouse gas emissions to a little more than 5% below their 1990 levels, by 2012. The vast majority of the world's countries have ratified the protocol, including Canada, the European countries, Japan, China and India. The United States has refused to ratify it for economic reasons.

The signing of the Kyoto Protocol in 1997.

Canada has a major challenge ahead, as it is the second largest producer of greenhouse gases per inhabitant in the world, and thus one of the worst polluters. Over the next few years, it must turn to non-polluting energy sources and encourage people to change their means of transportation.

Let's Get to Work!

1 Pandemics have periodically affected populations since the dawn of time.

a) Write down one factor that makes them less threatening today than they were in the past.

_____

_____

b) Write down one factor that makes them more threatening today than they were in the past.

_____

_____

2 Put a checkmark beside the correct statement about the Kyoto Protocol.

◯ The Kyoto Protocol aims to completely eliminate greenhouse gases.

◯ The Kyoto Protocol aims to reduce greenhouse gases.

◯ The countries that did not ratify the Kyoto Protocol refused because they are not affected by climate change.

3 a) While out shopping at the grocery store, you have to make a choice between Quebec apples and South American bananas. Explain what repercussions your choice will have on the environment.

_____

_____

_____

b) If you had the choice between Quebec apples treated with pesticides and other chemicals, and South American bananas that were certified organic, which would you choose? Justify your choice from an ecological point of view.

_____

_____

How Does Globalization Affect Culture?

Globalization gives us access to a staggering amount of information. What are the advantages and disadvantages of this limitless access to information? How do new methods of communication affect culture?

Advances in communications

With radio, television, telephone and the Internet, information can be sent right across the world at very low cost. These means of communication are very fast and are accessible to large numbers of people around the world.

Advantages of the Internet	Disadvantages of the Internet
• The Internet enables a very large number of people to have access to knowledge.	• There is so much information that users have to sift through it, and they need skills to tell which sources are trustworthy and which are not.
• A large amount of information is available through a single access point.	• It is difficult to regulate the kind of information available, as each country has its own laws regarding privacy, business and censorship.
• Electronic shopping via the Internet increases business.	• There is unequal Internet access between rural and urban areas, and between people who are literate and those who are not.
• The Internet helps poor regions develop by providing access to skills people might not otherwise have had (a network of farmers can exchange agricultural techniques via the Internet, for example).	• Downloading is so easy that it is hard to enforce copyright rules.

In January, 2006, 885 million music files were available on the Internet for illegal downloading.

7.10 *The Grande Bibliothèque du Québec.*

The Grande Bibliothèque du Québec has an online catalogue of several million documents. It also offers the public remote access to hundreds of thousands of digitized books and images.

Did you know... Did you know... Did yo

GLOBISH

There are about 6,800 languages spoken in the world, of which 200 are written. In this era of global communication, knowledge of one's mother tongue alone is no longer enough. Linguists have noticed the emergence of a "new language" called Globish (short for Global English). Containing fewer than 2,000 English words, it is a highly simplified language whose goal is to communicate only basic information.

Did you know... Did you know... Did y

The challenge of culture

Globalization facilitates the dissemination of culture (films, music, books, TV programs) throughout the world. Cultures meet and mix, influence one another, and change as they come in contact.

Cultural diversity

New methods of communication increase both cultural diversity and cultural homogeneity.

- People can use the new technologies to find out more about different cultures, which can be so easily and cheaply transmitted around the world. People can now record their own songs at home, for example, and make them available on the Internet.
- Cultures are increasingly similar as they conform more and more to the dominant American culture. American culture is particularly pervasive in film, television and music.

Many governments try to defend their own culture against foreign (especially American) cultural products, which threaten to overwhelm local production:

- by law, in Quebec, at least 65% of the songs played on French-language radio stations must be in French;
- the government of Canada gives tax credits to film companies and supports the Canadian Broadcasting Corporation, Telefilm Canada and the Canada Council for the Arts;
- in some countries, such as France and Turkey, a tax on every movie ticket is used to support local filmmakers.

Many countries, including Canada and France, believe that cultural products should be exempt from free trade agreements. The WTO and the United States do not agree. However, UNESCO (United Nations Educational, Scientific and Cultural Organization) has passed a resolution that aims to protect national cultural industries from foreign cultural products.

Let's Get to Work!

1 In your opinion, what would be the advantage of having everyone speak the same language?

_____

_____

2 Write down one advantage and one disadvantage of the new means of communication from the point of view of artists.

Advantage: _____

_____

Disadvantage: _____

_____

3 Write down two examples of policies that would protect a culture against the harmful effects of globalization.

- _____

_____

- _____

_____

How Does Globalization Affect Politics?

After city-states, great empires, and then nation-states (or countries), what types of political system can we expect to see in the future? Is democracy in danger? Should national citizenship be replaced by global citizenship?

International politics

Globalized trade mostly manages to escape government control. In fact, a country's economic policies are often determined by international negotiations. Canada, for example, is not allowed to subsidize its softwood lumber industry, as this would contravene the North American Free Trade Agreement (NAFTA) that Canada signed along with two other countries. At the same time, as the Internet is a global network, it is useless for a government to pass laws regulating Internet commerce if other countries do not pass the same laws.

There is no single supranational political organization that currently regulates environmental protection, the economy and security. Instead there are a multitude of overlapping international agreements. Ultimately, the power of organizations such as the United Nations and the International Monetary Fund (IMF) are limited. In addition, antiglobalization activists object to the way they are run, accusing them of being undemocratic. The way the world is organized politically has become extremely complex.

✴ THE INTERNATIONAL MONETARY FUND (IMF)

The International Monetary Fund is an international organization whose mandate is to help countries in financial difficulties. The IMF's money comes from its 184 member countries. The voting power of each country is proportional to its financial contribution. In other words, when the IMF makes a decision, the vote of a country that gives more money is worth more than the vote of one that gives less.

The IMF offers emergency loans to countries in difficulty. These loans are usually only given on condition that the beneficiary country restructure its economic and political system: privatization, the removal of customs duties, etc.

Reform of the UN

Economic concerns have become so dominant they they often take precedence over political ones. Private economic interests are becoming very powerful: some multinationals are richer than entire countries.

Many groups therefore believe the UN should be strengthened, or that a new international organization should be formed to make sure
– that there is greater social justice and less disparity in working conditions from country to country;
– that there is fairer distribution of wealth throughout the world.

They want this organization to be more democratic, and not dominated by the most powerful countries.

On the other hand, it is difficult to strengthen the role of the UN. Sometimes, democracy within an individual country and its citizens' right to self-determination can get in the way. What should the UN do, for example, if the majority of a member

Did you know... Did you know... Did you know

THE G8

The Group of Eight, or the G8, is a forum of eight of the richest countries in the world: the United States, Japan, Germany, the United Kingdom, France, Italy, Canada and Russia. These countries hold yearly summits to discuss global issues. For the past few years, during the summit, antiglobalization pressure groups have held massive demonstrations against the G8. They accuse it of trying to control the world without consulting other countries.

Did you know... Did you know... Did you know

---

supranational: with power beyond that of separate nations or countries.

7.11 *The UN General Assembly.*

country's population supports military intervention in another country, refuses to share part of its wealth with poorer countries, and refuses to pay for the environmental damage it causes?

"Allan Rock, Canadian Ambassador to the United Nations, thinks the time has come to demonstrate some political courage. 'Let's change this organization [the UN] from a cloud of hot air into a true parliament of the world,' said the former Minister of Justice. 'Let's give it back some real moral credibility. Basically, Canada is saying this: we respect national sovereignty, but sovereignty goes with responsibilities. If a country cannot protect, or refuses to protect, a segment of its population, then the international community has the right and the duty to act by helping those people.'"

Jocelyn Coulon, "Le Canada veut changer l'ONU" (Canada wants to change the UN), *L'Actualité*, October 1, 2005. Free translation.

Let's Get to Work!

1 Fill in the table below to create a profile of three international organizations.

	IMF	WTO	G8
Number of member countries			
Role			

2 Indicate whether each of the following situations would lead to a weakening or a strengthening of the UN's power.

	UN power weakened	UN power strengthened
Member countries agree that the UN should play the role of judge in settling trade disputes.		
World powers threaten to withdraw from the UN if it takes away their privileges.		
Member countries agree that legislation passed at the UN should take precedence over their own national laws.		
Member countries vote not to intervene in countries where human rights are under threat.		

Inquiry Conclusion

SUMMARIZE WHAT YOU HAVE LEARNED

To summarize what you have learned in this Inquiry, fill in the table below showing the advantages and disadvantages of globalization in the five areas you studied.

	Advantages	Disadvantages
The effects of economic globalization on rich countries		
The effects of economic globalization on poor countries		
The effects of globalization on health and the environment		
The effects of globalization on culture		
The effects of globalization on politics		

A

advocate: to speak or write in favour of a cause.

allowance: regular payment made to a person.

annul: declare a marriage invalid.

apartheid: Afrikaans word meaning "separation" (Afrikaans is a language spoken by white South Africans).

armaments: weapons.

B

bail: sum of money paid by prisoners for their release until tried in court.

bankrupt: said of a company that can no longer meet its payments.

barter: trade without the use of money.

basilica: title granted by the pope to certain very important churches.

Basque: from the Basque country, a region straddling the border between Spain and France.

Bible: sacred book of Christianity made up of the Old and New Testaments.

bourgeois: member of the French middle class, or town dweller; later used to refer to the class of merchants and industrialists.

boycott: to refuse to buy goods or services from a particular company or country.

C

canal: an artificial waterway created for navigation.

capital: money needed to finance and operate a business.

censor: to ban a newspaper, book, song, film, etc., or parts of one, because of the ideas it expresses.

charcoal: a fuel made of wood that has been burned in the absence of air.

charter: document that states a fundamental law.

chastity: abstinence from all sexual intercourse.

Christendom: the Christian world.

civil rights: rights guaranteed to all citizens by law.

civilian: person who is not in the armed forces.

civilize: raise a primitive society to a "superior" level.

clergy: the body of people who exercise religious ministry.

colony: territory ruled by another country.

condenser: a chamber in which steam is reduced to water through cooling.

conquistador: 16th-century Spanish conqueror.

constitution: fundamental law defining the structure of a government.

council: assembly convened by the pope to make major decisions concerning the Church.

court: group of attendants to the monarch.

customs duty: tax imposed on products that cross a border.

D

discrimination: treating a certain kind of people differently based on certain characteristics.

dissidence: a synonym for revolt or rebellion.

duties: government taxes on imports or exports.

E

economic neoliberalism: an ideology that opposes any restrictions on the global free market.

empire: group of colonies ruled by a single authority.

enlightened despot: absolute monarch who believes in the principles of the Enlightenment.

entrepreneur: someone who starts or organizes a business or a factory.

erudite: scholarly, well-educated.

Estates-General: an assembly of representatives of the three estates in the Ancien Régime.

excommunicate: expel from the Church.

F

firedamp: a combustible gas present in coal mines.

First Nations: term used in Canada for some indigenous groups.

frugal: simple, plain, not lavish.

G

genocide: deliberate destruction of an ethnic or religious group.

ghetto: place where Jews were confined.

H

heretic: person who holds an opinion contrary to the established beliefs of the Church.

hydrography: the science of mapping waterways.

I

idleness: the state of not working and spending all one's time in recreation.

import quota: maximum quantity of a product allowed to be imported.

indigenous peoples: native people, or the people who first inhabit a region.

Indochina: region of Asia comprising Laos, Cambodia and Vietnam.

indulgence: access to heaven granted to the faithful by the pope in return for a donation to the Church.

industrialization: development of manufacturing on a large scale.

invest: to put money into a company in order to make a profit.

ironmonger: metal merchant.

L

latitude: distance from the equator.

loom: a weaving machine.

M

mandate: role or task assigned to a person or organization.

manufacturing: transforming raw materials into finished products, usually with machines.

mechanization: the introduction of machinery into the production process.

medieval: of the Middle Ages.

merchant: trader who is involved in international commerce.

middleman: trader who buys from producers and sells to consumers.

missionary: someone who is sent out to convert people to his or her religion.

monarch: king or queen.

monopoly: absolute control of an economic sector, with no competitors.

mother country: the country of origin of settlers or colonists.

multinational: a corporation that operates in many countries.

N

nationalism: a movement in which a people demands recognition as a full-fledged nation, capable of self-government.

O

ore: rock containing valuable metal.

P

pact: synonym for contract, or agreement.

pagan: a person who practises a religion other than Christianity, Judaism or Islam.

pandemic: an epidemic that spreads over a very large area.

parliament: assembly with the power to make laws.

patron: wealthy person who provides artists with financial support.

philanthropist: a person who loves humankind and engages in activities to improve the quality of human life.

philosopher: thinker who investigates the nature of truth, existence and knowledge.

political right: the right to participate in public life.

polygamy: the custom of having more than one wife at the same time.

polytheist: someone who worships many gods.

proletariat: the class of workers who must sell their labour to survive.

propaganda: distribution of information aimed at convincing the public to accept particular ideas.

protectionism: measures such as tariffs and import quotas aimed at protecting a country's industries from foreign competition.

public life: influence or authority in the political system.

R

racism: discrimination or prejudice based on race.

ratify: synonym for approve.

raw materials: natural resources that are processed into manufactured goods.

refining: the process of purifying crude oil into petroleum products, such as gasoline.

reform: profound change in an institution with a view to improving it.

repression: use of violence against a rebel movement.

republic: in France, a form of government in which the three powers are separated and the leader is elected.

revolution: overthrow of the social order, often starting as a revolt against the established authority.

Roma: Gypsies.

S

Scandinavia: northern region of Europe consisting of Denmark, Sweden and Norway.

secular: not concerned with religion.

sedentary: living in one place; not nomadic.

seigneur: noble landowner in France.

segregation: the act of separating one group from the rest, usually as a form of discrimination.

self-determination: right of a people to govern themselves.

shipyard: a place where ships are built.

smelt: to melt ore in order to extract the metal.

social class: group of people with the same economic position in society.

spin: to draw out and twist wool or cotton fibres to make thread for weaving.

spiritual: to do with the spirit or soul.

spoils: goods or property seized by a victor in wartime.

stockpile: to gather a large supply of valuable goods.

strike: workers refusing to work with the aim of achieving better working conditions.

subject: a person who is under the authority of a king.

subsidy: government aid to a business.

suffrage: synonym for voting.

supranational: with power beyond that of separate nations or countries.

T

tax: the money a government collects to pay for public expenses.

textiles: synonym for cloth; the cloth manufacturing industry.

theologian: thinker who studies God and divine truth.

thesis: position that a person is committed to defending in public.

Third World: synonym for developing countries.

tithe: a tenth of the annual agricultural produce given in support of the clergy.

trade union: an association of workers with the aim of protecting their interests.

trust: company which has a monopoly.

tsarina: feminine of tsar.

U

urbanization: the process of people increasingly moving into towns.

W

weave: to cross threads over one another to make fabric.

Y

yield: the size of the harvest in relation to the surface cultivated.